the mediterranean
REFRESH
MEAL PLAN

the mediterranean
REFRESH
MEAL PLAN

Erika Simons

peapil

CONTENTS

Introduction

Welcome to your Mediterranean Meal Plan! This "Healthy Eating" program is based on the Mediterranean Diet and will help detox the body and gain increased health and unbelievable weight loss.

We believe that optimal health can be attained through preventative measures by eating a wide range of fresh "real" food, rich in nutrients, which is what the Mediterranean Diet is all about. The Mediterranean Diet is hailed by many health experts around the world as the most universally beneficial diet for long-term health. This way of eating not only promotes foods rich in omega-3 and foods that are rich in fiber, vitamins, minerals and antioxidants (all of which promote good health) but it is generally easy to follow without having to stick to a set of strict rules as many other diets require.

We are so excited you are here and about to commence this 8-week program. You will eliminate the foods that cause many issues now and later in life, while focusing on nutrient-rich foods (typical of the Mediterranean Diet) that will support your living your best life.

While doing this program, you will also develop health-promoting eating habits that provide the foundations for a life of vitality and longevity. Throughout this program you will see the emphasis is on eating plenty of plant-based foods, consisting of a wide variety of vegetables, herbs, nuts, seeds, legumes and selected fruits. Red meat is limited to a serving or two a week, but you will have fish and poultry at least twice as often. Healthy fats are an important focus in the Mediterranean Diet and have been incorporated into most meals. We will discuss healthy fats in greater detail in the coming weeks.

Before beginning this 8-week program, it is important that you take note of the following:

Depending on what your current diet is like (for instance, if you are eating a lot of processed foods), you may feel withdrawal symptoms such as headaches, nausea, weakness or tiredness for the first 2 to 7 days. This is your body getting rid of stored toxins. It is highly recommended you drink at least 3 liters (or ¾ of a gallon) of water each day to support the elimination of these toxins.

Whether you are cooking for just yourself or the whole family, make sure you plan ahead. Pay attention to the serving sizes of each recipe and adjust preparation accordingly.

Take note of what you already have available at home and make up your shopping list with this in mind. Pick one day to go grocery shopping and then another for food prep if you wish to do meal planning ahead of time. Buy only the foods you require for the week ahead and make sure you store them correctly. If possible, purchase your grains, legumes, nuts, seeds and other dry produce in bulk to cut costs.

Follow the meal plans carefully. While each ingredient has been carefully selected to provide a balance of nutrients, the recipes are also versatile. For example, feel free to make smart substitutions with ingredients you've already got on hand. You can swap feta with ricotta if that is what's available, or kale for spinach. Be sure to use whatever you already have before racing out to buy extra ingredients that may not be necessary.

If you like to have a snack between meals, make sure you're nibbling on whole real food. Some snack suggestions are vegetables sticks with hummus, olives, avocado on rice crackers, Greek yogurt with a piece of fresh fruit, or a small handful of mixed nuts and seeds. For more snack ideas that are Mediterranean-friendly, refer to our copy of *The Mediterranean Refresh*.

Do not skip meals. You should not feel hungry if you stick to the eating plan. If you skip a meal, it may increase your hunger hormones and will be counterproductive. Also do your best not to eat anything after 7 p.m. This will help with your metabolism.

Herbs are a wonderful source of nutrients and can assist with detoxification and achieving optimal health. Feel free to add a wide variety of fresh herbs (organic or homegrown whenever possible) to your meals.

Essential Elements of the Mediterranean Diet

In a nutshell, the Mayo Clinic emphasizes three major points about the Mediterranean Diet:

1. Eating primarily plant-based foods, such as fruits, vegetables, whole grains, legumes and nuts

2. Replacing butter with healthy fats such as olive oil and canola oil.

3. Using herbs and spices instead of salt to flavor foods.

Note that the diet doesn't require eliminating fat from your diet. Many food trends like the keto and paleo diets actually recommend fat, and this diet is no different. It's overall less restrictive in that it believes in fresh foods, whole grains and legumes.

Use Olive Oil

Olive oil is the primary source of fat in this diet. It provides monounsaturated fat—a type that reduces LDL (bad) cholesterol levels. We recommend extra-virgin olive oil because it has the highest levels of the plant compounds that actually provide antioxidant effects.

Recent research indicates that olive oil protects against chronic diseases and helps in the battle against diabetes, obesity and cancer. Owing to its cardioprotective role, olive oil provides antihypertensive, antithrombotic, antioxidant, anti-inflammatory and anticarcinogenic action.

This diet isn't about limiting total fat consumption, but rather about making good choices regarding which fats to choose. To enjoy the diet's fullest benefits, avoid saturated fats and hydrogenated oils, which contain trans fats. These unhealthy fats are tied to heart disease and will counteract all the healing that your body is otherwise undergoing.

Eat Fish

Even if you're not a fish lover, there are plenty of delicious recipes to experiment with. Fish is a rich source of omega-3 fatty acids. The fish in this diet is cooked fresh and never deep fried. Don't worry, there is plenty of direction in the recipe section of this book.

Enjoy Wine Time

The health effects of wine have been debated forever, but most experts agree that as long as you don't drink excessively, wine can be a wonderful component of a healthy diet. If you choose to drink wine, we recommend limiting your consumption to 5 ounces per day for those over the age of 65, and 10 ounces per day for those under 65.

Go Nuts

Nuts are another vital food group in the Mediterranean Diet. They contain beneficial linolenic acid (a type of omega-3 fatty acid). Omega-3 fatty acids lower triglycerides, decrease blood clotting and may lower the risk of a sudden heart attack, improve the health of your blood vessels and help moderate blood pressure.

Nuts are high in fat, but most of it is not saturated fat. Make sure not to eat too many—about a handful a day. Also avoid corner-store candied nuts.

I recommend unsalted nuts, and I especially love fresh walnuts, pistachios and almonds. Cashews are also a tasty and healthy choice.

Replacing your regular snacks with fresh nuts is a great way to reduce empty calories and avoid added sugar and sodium. Nuts are also a great source of fiber and minerals like potassium, which makes them a much better choice than processed snack foods.

Eat Veggies and Fruit

Make sure to always include a handful of veggies with every dish you prepare. Don't be afraid to serve a piece of fruit for dessert or add it to a recipe for an extra bit of natural sweetness. In general, always pick fresh fruit over anything with processed sugar. One of the best parts of this diet is hitting up the local farmer's markets and choosing what to eat based on the season's offerings. I've found it's a wonderful way to educate my children, and they love going!

A good rule of thumb: eat veggies all day long, with every meal. It's simply the best way to get extra nutrients and fill your tummy without a ton of calories, and veggies have actually been proved to reduce stress.

Fruit is the best way to satisfy your sweet tooth. Fruit contains fiber and sugar that is naturally occurring, which means it won't spike your blood sugar nearly as much as the same amount of added sugar would. Full of vitamin C and antioxidants, fruit is a great way to complete a well-balanced diet.

Switch to Whole Grains

This is such a simple way to increase the amount of fiber and nutrition in your diet. I always recommend whole grains for a delicious, guilt-free pasta dish.

Ingredients used in the Mediterranean region are typically made from whole grains and contain very few trans fats. Bread is important to the diet but is never served with butter or margarine. It's best to avoid these because they contain trans fats.

Eat Less Red Meat

Substitute fish and poultry for red meat. When you do choose red meat, try to make the portions small. And always opt for fresh meat over preserved or processed meats like sausage and beef jerky.

Choose Low-Fat, No-Sugar Dairy

We recommend low-fat yogurt with no added sugar. It's an easy way to get all the benefits of dairy without the baggage.

Add Spices

Spices are full of nutrients and anti-inflammatory properties—not to mention the fact that spices can make any dish ten times more delicious. When going through the recipes, take note of which spices and herbs we recommend. Try to get good at knowing how much you like to add, and which ones are your favorites. Using spices wisely can also help you reduce the amount of added sugar you need in your recipes.

If you're curious about the types of spices that work best with the Mediterranean Diet, I recommend our own *Mediterranean Refresh proprietary spice blends* that can be found on Amazon.com.

Tips for Success

Before you get started on the Mediterranean Diet, it's a good idea to do a little bit of preparation. Oftentimes when we jump right into things, it's easy to become overwhelmed. So read on a bit and familiarize yourself with some of the basic principles before diving into any of the recipes. Unless, of course, you just need something fun to eat—then feel free to pick out an inviting recipe and get started right away.

Adapt Your Current Diet

Before diving into the diet completely, take a quick look at what you currently enjoy and try to make subtle changes. Reduce the amount of red meat you're consuming. Start cooking with olive oil. Try switching to low-fat yogurt. Decrease the number of sugary treats. See if you can't morph your current menus into the Mediterranean Diet instead of starting from scratch. Slowly moving toward this diet will make it harder to go back to less desirable habits.

Learn to make some simple substitutions. Instead of consuming a bag of chips, grab a fistful of nuts. Find something in the Mediterranean Diet that will make a healthy replacement for some of your less beneficial choices.

I've included whole sections on snack foods, drinks and even desserts to help you on your path. Take a look at those sections right now and think about which recipes would be a great substitute for some of the things you're eating already.

Your New Food Pyramid

This food pyramid was developed by the Mediterranean Diet Foundation Expert Group and shows which foods you should eat as part of the diet. Every recipe in the book closely follows this pyramid.

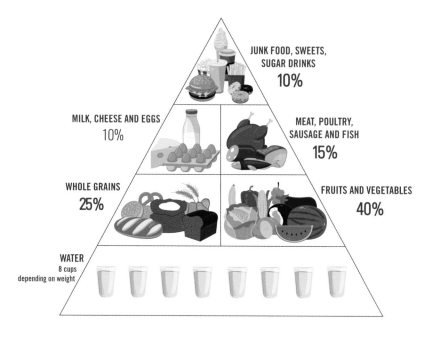

Here are the basic percentages of each food group you should aim for each day, based on the Mediterranean Food Pyramid:

Water	7-8 cups a day (8-oz)
Fresh Fruits and Vegetables	40% • Try to opt for fresh, seasonal fruits and veggies. If you're ever hungry, just know you can eat more veggies!
Whole Grains	25%
Dairy Products	10%
Meat, Poultry and Fish	15% • Always choose poultry over red meat.If serving red meat, make portions small.
Junk Food and Sweets	10%

The Pantry

In order to maintain this diet, it's important to stock up on the ingredients that are used in most of the recipes. It's always a good idea to have lots of fruits, vegetables, and nuts on hand as they go well with each Mediterranean dish. That way you're not running to the grocery store every day! I also made sure that each recipe in this book uses common ingredients, so you won't have to trek to specialty shops to try to find obscure items. No special equipment or appliances are needed either.

And don't leave temptation in sight! Everything you buy at the grocery store will end up in your stomach… so make sure you leave that tantalizing bag of chips at the store. It's so much harder to avoid indulgence when the food is right next to you, waiting to be devoured. How often have you heard yourself say, "I wouldn't eat this, but it's going to go bad… so I have to!" It happens to me all the time.

Take a good look at your pantry and fridge. Review the information on pages 12–16, and try to give away or toss out ingredients such as your less healthy oils and margarine. I know it can be hard, and it may seem like a big waste of money. But the benefits of making a clean switch to this healthier way of living are way more valuable than the unhealthy food you need to get rid of.

Enjoy the Vacation

Take your time. Remember when I said the Mediterranean Diet is like eating as if you're on vacation? One of the core tenets of the diet is to take things slowly when dining. Instead of shoving food down as quickly as possible after going through a drive-through or mindlessly eating while watching Netflix, we invite you to sit down at the table with your family and friends. Slowly enjoy and savor what you're eating.

Gathering with friends and family, in fact, and enjoying a freshly made meal is a vital part of the Mediterranean culture. Taking the time to share a meal with your loved ones, talking about the day and enjoying one another's presence is an amazing experience.

Not only will you enjoy the food better but eating slowly allows you to pay attention to what's going into your mouth. It's good to get an awareness of when you're truly full to prevent overeating. Consuming smaller portions is the easiest way to reduce weight, so be prepared to stop eating when you're satisfied. So often we end up eating until we need to start undoing our belts! Really pay attention while you eat slowly—take notes on what changes you'd like to make to a particular recipe in the future.

Exercise (Argh!)

No lifestyle book would be complete without a little side note about exercise. Thankfully, if you go to our online community, you'll find dozens of resources that will help people just like you go on to a more active lifestyle. I invite you to visit our community today!

Try to get about 20 minutes of exercise every day. One "cheat" I use is to always take the stairs. I also make sure to park far away from the entrance to the grocery store when I go shopping.

Little things like this force you to get in a bit of exercise. I've also tried to get more involved with my daughter's activities. Instead of sending her to dance class, I've actually joined a mom-daughter class so we can work out together! It's so much more fun than just watching her dance, and I get to learn along with her and enjoy some exercise at the same time!

Introducing Week One!

Get familiar with this week's recipes and those of the weeks ahead. Start to become familiar with the layout of each week's plan and what is required for prep.

Work out what your weekly routine is going to be like. What days are you going to do your inventory of the foods you have on hand and develop a shopping list? When will your shopping day be, and do you require a meal prep day? Set yourself up for success with a clear, organized plan.

Final Word

Have fun! The most important thing about this program is to enjoy it and have fun while you're taking part! Healthy eating is meant to be exciting and simple. There is no need to stress about it or make things too complicated. We suggest that you follow each week's recipes as best you can and pay attention to our outlined notes above and stick to some basic rules. That way you will head off on a healthy eating regime that your body will not only thank you for but that you can easily sustain for a lifetime.

Disclaimer

The program is based on healthy eating and removing unhealthy foods. This program does not constitute medical advice. If you require advice in relation to any matter, you should consult an appropriate health professional. In particular, if you have a chronic disease or are on prescribed medication, check with your doctor before starting this program. Make sure you exclude any foods that you are allergic to.

WEEK

1

	SUNDAY	MONDAY	TUESDAY
	Lemon Ricotta Pancakes (PAGE 111) *(Be sure to prepare the ricotta cheese the night before as per recipe)	Golden Millet Porridge (PAGE 109)	Fruit Salad with Italian Ricotta (PAGE 108)
	Spinach Torta (PAGE 140)	Rustic Avocado and Corn Salad (PAGE 188)	Falafel Tortillas with Tahini Sauce (PAGE 191) *(Double the amount of falafel and tahini sauce required for this meal. You will use them again for dinner on Wednesday)
	Meat Loaf Stuffed with Prosciutto & Cheese (PAGE 195) *Serve with* Simple Greek Salad (PAGE 131)	Moroccan Vegetable Tagine (PAGE 151)	Mediterranean Baked Cod with Lemon & Garlic (PAGE 147)

WEEK

WEDNESDAY	THURSDAY	FRIDAY	SATURDAY
Gourmet Feta Toast (PAGE 110) *(Substitute the Italian ricotta for the feta as you already have it on your grocery list. But if you also have feta on hand, feel free to use it instead as per recipe)*	Sun Smoothie (PAGE 209)	Overnight Breakfast Strata (PAGE 113)	Stuffed Mushrooms (PAGE 115)
Neapolitan Polenta Pie (PAGE 199)	Avgolemono Lemon Chicken Soup (PAGE 119)	Chicken Souvlaki with Tzatziki (PAGE 120)	Grilled Salmon on Herbed Couscous (PAGE 136)
Leftover Falafel (PAGE 191) *Serve with* Simple Greek Salad (PAGE 131)	Seafood Paella (PAGE 153)	Caprese Chicken (PAGE 186)	Roasted Lamb Rack with Velvet-Black Olive Sauce (PAGE 202) *(Reserve the leftover roast lamb for next week's Saturday dinner meal plan. Store in an airtight container in the fridge)*
			NOTE: It's Saturday night—treat yourself to a glass or two of wine and a square of dark chocolate.

WEEK

1

Shopping List

Vegetables

- 1 lb. arugula
- 3 avocados
- 4 bell peppers
- 1 butternut squash
- 1 lb. carrots
- 1 lb. celery
- 2 oz. chives
- 1 lb. corn
- 1 large cucumber
- 8 oz. green beans
- 1 lb. green onions
- 2 lb. lettuce (mixed greens)
- 1 lb. mushrooms
- 2 lb. potatoes
- 1 lb. red onions
- 2 scallions
- 1 lb. spinach
- 2 lb. yellow onions
- 2 lb. zucchini

Fruit

- 3 apples
- 4 oz. cherry tomato
- 2 lemons
- 2 Nashi pears
- 2 pomegranate arils
- 3 medium tomatoes

Protein

- 4 lb. chicken breast
- 4 oz. chorizo
- 2 cod fillets
- 6 eggs
- 1 lb. flounder
- 1 lb. ground beef
- 1 lb. ground pork
- 2 lamb racks
- 1 lb. prawns
- 2 oz. prosciutto
- 4 salmon fillets
- 2 sausages

Pantry Items

(make sure you have at least the following on hand)

- ½ cup balsamic vinegar
- 1 cup black olives
- 4 oz. canned green lentils
- 2 oz. capers
- 2 qt. chicken stock
- 8 oz. chickpeas
- 1 cup couscous
- ¼ cup Dijon mustard
- 2 oz. dried apricots
- ½ cup dried cranberries
- 4 oz. flaxseed sprouts
- ½ cup honey
- ½ cup lemon juice
- 4 oz. millet

- ○ 8 oz. oats
- ○ 1 cup olive oil
- ○ 4 oz. pearl barley
- ○ 4 oz. polenta
- ○ ¼ cup prepared mustard
- ○ 6 oz. raisins
- ○ 12 oz. rice
- ○ 4 oz. sun-dried tomatoes
- ○ ½ cup tahini (sesame paste)
- ○ 1 can tomatoes
- ○ 2 cans tuna
- ○ 2 qt. vegetable stock
- ○ ¼ cup walnuts
- ○ ¼ cup white wine vinegar
- ○ 1 cup whole-wheat flour
- ○ ¼ cup Worcestershire sauce

Dry Herbs, Spices and Baking Needs

- ○ baking powder
- ○ basil
- ○ bay leaves
- ○ black pepper
- ○ cilantro
- ○ dried marjoram
- ○ dried mustard
- ○ dried oregano leaves
- ○ dried porcini mushrooms
- ○ fennel seeds
- ○ flour
- ○ garlic powder
- ○ ground cinnamon
- ○ ground cumin
- ○ Italian dried herbs
- ○ lemon verbena
- ○ mint
- ○ oregano

- ○ paprika
- ○ parsley
- ○ rosemary sprigs
- ○ saffron
- ○ salt
- ○ sugar
- ○ thyme

Dairy *(substitute as needed)*

- ○ butter
- ○ feta cheese
- ○ Greek feta cheese
- ○ Greek yogurt
- ○ Italian ricotta cheese
- ○ milk
- ○ mozzarella cheese
- ○ Parmesan cheese
- ○ ricotta cheese

Bakery and Frozen Items

- ○ bread crumbs
- ○ pie crust
- ○ sourdough bread
- ○ toast
- ○ tortillas

Alcohol Used for Cooking

- ○ Madeira wine
- ○ white wine

WEEK

2

Introduction

Welcome to Week 2 of your Mediterranean Meal Plan. We hope you are enjoying this healthy and delicious way of eating!

The diet, as you will begin to see, is all about fresh, "real" food, with very limited processed foods. While you're following this program, we want to teach you how you can maintain this way of eating for good.

One of the best ways to reduce your consumption of processed foods and to eat a daily diet rich in nutrients is to make sure you have a pantry well stocked with the appropriate ingredients. Items such as ancient grains, beans, legumes, spices, nuts, seeds, healthy oils, and natural sweeteners like raw honey are just a few items that should become staples in your kitchen. From these kinds of individual ingredients, you can make an unlimited number of healthy meals that will not just taste amazing but also provide many nutritional benefits. When you have a good supply of quality healthy ingredients on hand, it is so easy to be organized and stay committed to healthy eating.

To create a pantry stocked with health-promoting ingredients, we suggest you just start one step at a time (there's no need to go and throw out every item in your kitchen that may not be that great)! Simply begin by replacing ingredients of concern (that may, for instance, cause inflammation—more on that later) such as vegetable cooking oil with olive oil, and margarine with butter. Make one swap per week. That way you'll have a pantry full of healthy alternatives in no time. Find below some of our top suggestions for easy "real food" swaps that will go hand in hand with this Mediterranean meal plan.

Try and focus on whole foods and olive oil as much as possible.

SOMETIMES	OFTEN
Margarine, vegetable oil, canola oil, corn oil, soybean oil, rice bran oil	Extra-virgin olive oil, coconut oil, ghee, butter, avocado oil, macadamia oil, flaxseed oil
Conventional milk, light and skim varieties	Unpasteurized whole cream, milk, coconut milk, almond milk or another nut milk
Conventional eggs and meat	Free-range and/or grass-fed, lean varieties
White bread	Organic sourdough bread, whole-meal and seeded breads, puffed rice cakes or corn cakes, nori sheets (can use as wraps)

SOMETIMES	OFTEN
White sugar and refined/ artificial sweeteners	Honey, pure maple syrup, stevia, coconut sugar, Medjool dates
White flour	Organic, unbleached flour, spelt flour, coconut flour, almond meal
Table salt	Sea salt, Himalayan pink salt
Sugary drinks	Fresh smoothies, freshly squeezed juices, lime/ lemon in soda water
Processed sauces, dressing and/ or marinades	Fresh homemade varieties
Conventional cereals	Oats, buckwheat, quinoa porridge, chia seed pudding, Bircher muesli, granola

Hot Tip for Week 2

Continue to take stock of what you already have available at home and adjust your shopping list accordingly. You may start to notice that you already have many of the same or similar ingredients you need for following the Mediterranean Diet. You may also have leftover ingredients from last week's purchases so make sure you cross them off this week's shopping list. Buy only the foods you require for the week ahead and see that you store them correctly to preserve their shelf life.

Suggestions of ways to adjust to your new eating habits and cope with cravings:

A new way of eating can be exciting—you may be feeling positive. However, we understand it may not always be easy. You may have already struggled with curbing your appetite and other cravings. In these moments it's best to have an established game plan. We suggest you write a list of some alternative things you can do instead of succumbing to temptation in moments of weakness. Place that list on your fridge and when you feel you may be struggling and want to gobble down something that may not benefit your health, pick an item from your list to do instead. Here are some ideas:

Make a cup of herbal tea and go sip it outside in the sunshine

Distract yourself by keeping busy—for instance, do some gardening, start a project, set out a list of any tasks/goals you would like to achieve and make a start on them

Go for a walk

Call a friend

Take a bath

Whatever it is you may come up with, the idea is to create a practical list of things to do to help replace old unhealthy habits.

This week let's introduce Lemon Water. This healthy concoction alkalizes your body and helps flush out toxins. Moreover, it boosts your metabolism and "resets" your appetite. Some say it can even curb sugar cravings. All you need to do is squeeze half a lemon in a glass of water and drink it the first thing in the morning.

Eat regularly and mindfully. Sticking to a meal plan and keeping clear of foods that aren't going to do you any favors is easier when you eat regularly throughout the day. Try to consume your meals at the same time each day and learn to eat mindfully, meaning you're aware of what you're taking in and are alive in the moment. Focus on what's happening right now and enjoy food with all your senses. Turn off your cell phone, TV and laptop. Sit down and savor your meals. It is also important to learn to recognize the difference between physical and emotional hunger. Don't eat when you're stressed, angry or bored. Keep yourself distracted (refer to that list on your fridge) until those feelings go away. Your emotions can influence appetite.

This Week's Goal

Take stock of your pantry and start a list of the "simple healthy swaps" you can begin to make in the weeks ahead.

Create your list of alternative activities for the times you may be struggling with a craving or with "emotional" eating and stick it on your fridge.

Each mealtime make sure you take the time to enjoy your foods—their flavors, colors, and textures—and to savor every bite.

Final Word

Don't forget to continue to have fun. Prepare what you can ahead of time to take the stress and chaos out of mealtimes. Always remember that food is not your enemy. It's fuel for your mind and body. Whole, natural foods provide you with the energy that you need to function at your peak.

SUNDAY	MONDAY	TUESDAY
Tortilla Española (PAGE 116) **(Omit the Italian sausage from this recipe for a vegetarian meal. Cook as per recipe—just without the sausage)*	Greek Yogurt Smoothie (PAGE 212)	Golden Millet Porridge (PAGE 109)
Shrimp & Asparagus Salad (PAGE 138)	Portuguese Chorizo Soup (PAGE 201)	Sicilian Eggplant Caponata (PAGE 139) *Serve with* Simple Greek Salad (PAGE 131)
Mediterranean Meatballs (PAGE 197)	Shrimp & Leek Spaghetti (PAGE 169)	Panko Salmon with Snap Peas (PAGE 170)
	NOTE: If you're after a quick and easy lunch tomorrow, you can also prepare the caponata tonight to be ready for Tuesday's lunch. Store in an airtight container in the fridge.	

WEEK

2

WEDNESDAY	THURSDAY	FRIDAY	SATURDAY
Gourmet Feta Toast (PAGE 110)	Overnight Breakfast Strata (PAGE 113)	Breakfast Fig Smoothie (PAGE 103)	Easy Breakfast Pizza (PAGE 106)
Italian Oven-Roasted Vegetables (PAGE 122)	Zesty Lemon Rice (PAGE 123)	Tuna-Stuffed Eggplants (PAGE 142) *(Use grated Parmesan cheese for the grated cheese in this recipe unless you have another grated cheese on hand you would prefer)	Mediterranean Bean Salad (PAGE 124)
Chicken Piccata (PAGE 189) *(If you don't have demi-glace, use chicken stock)	Fish in Island Sauce (PAGE 193)	Pasta Salad with Tomatoes & Eggplant (PAGE 173)	Falafel Tortillas with Tahini Sauce (PAGE 191)
			NOTES: Take time out of today to make a double batch of the Cottage Cheese Blueberry Casserole. It's for breakfast on tomorrow and needs to be made ahead of time. It's Saturday night— treat yourself to a glass or two of wine and a square of dark chocolate.

WEEK 2

Shopping List

Vegetables

- 1 lb. arugula
- 2 lb. asparagus
- 3 avocados
- 8 oz. baby sweet peas
- 1 butternut squash
- 1 lb. carrots
- 1 lb. celery
- 2 oz. chives
- 8 oz. green beans
- 1 lb. green onions
- 1 large cabbage
- 1 large cucumber
- 2 lb. lettuce (mixed greens)
- 1 lb. mushrooms
- 4 bell peppers
- 2 lb. potatoes
- 1 lb. red onions
- 2 scallions
- 1 lb. spinach
- 2 lb. yellow onions
- 2 lb. zucchini

Fruit

- 4 oz. fresh figs
- 4 frozen bananas
- 2 lemons
- 4 oz. cherry tomato
- 3 medium tomatoes
- 2 Nashi pears
- 2 pomegranate arils

Protein

- 2 cod fillets
- 6 eggs
- 1 lb. flounder
- 1 lb. ground beef
- 1 lb. ground pork
- 2 lamb racks
- 8 oz. lobster
- 1 lb. prawns
- 2 oz. prosciutto
- 4 salmon fillets
- 2 sausages

Pantry

- ½ cup balsamic vinegar
- 1 cup black olives
- 4 oz. canned green lentils
- 2 oz. capers
- 2 qt. chicken stock
- 8 oz. chickpeas
- 1 cup couscous
- 2 oz. dried apricots
- ½ cup dried cranberries
- 4 oz. flaxseed sprouts
- ½ cup honey
- ½ cup lemon juice
- 4 oz. millet

- 8 oz. oats
- 1 cup olive oil
- 4 oz. pearl barley
- 4 oz. polenta
- ¼ cup prepared mustard
- 6 oz. raisins
- 12 oz. rice
- 4 oz. sundried tomatoes
- ½ cup tahini (sesame paste)
- 1 can tomatoes
- 2 cans tuna
- 2 qt. vegetable stock
- ¼ cup walnuts
- ¼ cup white wine vinegar
- 1 cup whole-wheat flour
- ¼ cup Worcestershire sauce

Dry Herbs, Spices and Baking Needs

- baking powder
- basil
- bay leaves
- black pepper
- cilantro
- dried marjoram
- dried oregano leaves
- dried porcini mushrooms
- fennel seed
- garlic powder
- lemon verbena
- mint
- oregano
- paprika

- parsley
- rosemary sprigs
- saffron
- salt
- sugar
- thyme

Dairy

- butter
- cream cheese
- feta cheese
- Greek yogurt
- heavy cream
- Italian ricotta
- milk
- mozzarella cheese
- Parmesan cheese
- ricotta cheese

Bakery and Frozen Items

- bread crumbs
- pie crust
- sourdough bread
- toast
- tortillas

Alcohol Used for Cooking

- white wine

Introduction

Welcome to Week 3 of your Mediterranean Meal Plan. We trust that you can start to reap the many benefits this program has to offer.

As you will now begin to learn, and experience, a healthy diet can have a noticeable effect on how you feel both physically and emotionally. A natural, low-processed meal plan such as the Mediterranean Diet will reduce levels of inflammation, which in turn will make you feel great, increase your quality of life and reduce the risk of many chronic diseases.

Introduction to Inflammation—Don't Shoot the Messenger!

When something harmful or irritating affects our body, the body generates an immune response to try to protect itself and remove the offender—this is what is known as inflammation. The presence of inflammation makes a person susceptible to illness and disease and often occurs years before it becomes apparent. There are a multitude of factors that cause inflammation, with poor diet being number one!

It is important to take the time to note any ailments you may have previously had or are currently experiencing. Sometimes we forget or may not yet have taken notice of what may be bothering us.

Action!

Take time NOW to listen to and recognize what your body is saying! Furthermore, start to listen to what your body is telling you after *every* time you eat. It can be these signs are telegraphing what foods are causing inflammation, leading to "Dis-Ease" in the body. For example, do you get a runny nose after consuming dairy, feel tired after gluten, have stomach cramps or become bloated after wheat or experience mood swings after sugary drinks? What is this telling you? It is up to YOU to listen to your body and notice what indicators are informing you when inflammation occurs. Becoming aware of these things will allow you to choose which foods your body can tolerate, and enable you to live a life of vitality and longevity.

Inflammation left unattended in the body can lead to numerous, serious and debilitating diseases. We don't want that now, do we?

Take note of any of the following symptoms you may have witnessed in the past or may be currently experiencing:

- Bloating
- Reflux
- Heartburn
- Constipation
- Diarrhea
- Irritable bowel
- Mood swings
- Hot flushes
- Tiredness/fatigue
- Headaches/migraines

- Aching joints
- Muscle cramps
- Achy back
- Sore knees
- Fluid retention
- Flaky/itchy skin
- Excess mucus
- Throat irritation
- Coughing after eating
- Constant clearing of the throat

Recommendations for Reducing or Eliminating Inflammatory Foods

When following a diet rich in nutrient-dense foods as previously outlined, you will find that nutritionally empty foods and inflammatory foods will naturally start to disappear from your menus. It is important, however, to know what foods to reduce to a minimum or eliminate altogether. These are primarily foods that may cause you inflammation or create irritating or harmful effects. Here are some recommendations and suggestions to recognize the major culprits:

For most people dairy is highly inflammatory, although it may form a large part of their diet. Foods such as cheese, milk and yogurt (don't forget the milk in your coffee or tea) can be present in almost every meal of the day. If you experience symptoms such as mucus, asthma, allergies, joint pain, nerve pain, arthritis or hay fever while consuming dairy, this may mean dairy is not for you. Signs like these can indicate your immune system has gone into overload. An overconsumption of dairy can be a cause of these inflammatory triggers. It is best to reduce it in your diet and choose better sources such as plain natural yogurt or kefir and unpasteurized, fresh full cream milk.

Wheat is another food that can be highly inflammatory, and that is causing more and more people to become intolerant. This is primarily due to the way it is grown, harvested and processed in today's modern age. If you find wheat is irritating for you, it is best to eliminate or reduce significantly it in your diet.

When choosing a bread, try to select only preservative-free bread, especially something without the additive 282. You could also try rye bread or spelt bread—just make sure it is wheat-free. Better yet, bake your own, using quality ingredients.

Avoid conventional breakfast cereals as well as cakes, muffins, biscuits, store-bought sandwiches, pies and pastries. These types of foods not only contain wheat but they will also be filled with many other inflammatory ingredients such as refined sugar, vegetable oil and preservatives. For a treat, aim for homemade varieties or, when dining out, look for gluten-free options wherever possible.

Reduce the consumption of any processed foods in your diet, including deli meats, bottled sauces, TV dinners, preprepared meals, packet soups, noodles, premade marinades, chips, etc. Make eliminating packaged products a top priority—prepare what you can yourself from real ingredients.

Avoid soft drinks, cordials, flavored milks, store-bought fruit juice, iced teas, energy drinks, and the like. These drinks are very high in sugar. Drink plenty of water each day, a minimum of two liters or 7-8 glasses.

Limit caffeinated drinks such as coffee and tea to 1 to 2 cups per day, and aim to drink them no later than 6 p.m. Try to introduce fruit teas, green tea or herbal teas as an alternative option. You can enjoy these as much as you like and drink them at any time of the day.

If consuming alcohol, try not to average more than one drink every day. Aim to have at least two alcohol-free days per week—this will help your body in remove any stored toxins. When choosing an alcoholic beverage, look for pure distilled varieties such as a good-quality vodka or gin. Whenever possible, choose organic and/or preservative-free wines.

Hot Tip for Week 3

Start learning to read labels on all foods that are too difficult (or you don't have the time) to make yourself and you will need to purchase. The general rule of thumb is that if you can't recognize an ingredient, chances are your body won't either and won't know how to process it. This may lead to an inflammatory response. Select the product/brand that has the fewest ingredients and that seems to use the most "real" natural foods.

This Week's Goals

Take note of any/all inflammatory responses or conditions you may have experienced/suffered in the past. Start a food diary: list any triggers that occur after a particular meal and see if a pattern starts to develop. For example, do you feel bloated whenever you eat wheat, or do you start to sneeze every time you consume dairy? These could be red flags.

Take a look in your fridge and pantry and get familiar with your labels. Take some time out to read whatever is in your products. Are there any surprises?

Final Word

Don't forget that the most powerful way to fight off inflammation is through the foods we eat. Choosing the right foods will significantly reduce your risk of illness and chronic disease, while ensuring that at the same time you feel great! Consistently picking foods that trigger negative responses (don't forget, your body will tell you which ones those are) can accelerate inflammatory processes in the body and leave you susceptible to disease.

	SUNDAY	MONDAY	TUESDAY
	Cottage Cheese Blueberry Casserole (PAGE 105)	Golden Millet Porridge (PAGE 109)	Sun Smoothie (PAGE 209)
	Tuscan Sausage & Bean Soup (PAGE 145)	Bulgur & Lime Tabouli (PAGE 125)	Rustic Avocado and Corn Salad (PAGE 188)
	Zucchini, Pesto & Sausage Pizza (PAGE 175)	Italian Meatball Wedding Soup (PAGE 184)	Chicken & Cucumber Salad with Parsley Pesto (PAGE 176)

WEEK

3

NOTE:

Tomorrow's lunch requires cooked quinoa. To save time, prepare a batch of quinoa tonight (according to packet directions) and store in the fridge to use tomorrow.

WEDNESDAY	THURSDAY	FRIDAY	SATURDAY
Spanish Breakfast Beans (PAGE 114) *(Make double the amount required so you can serve again on Friday)*	Caprese Breakfast Tart (PAGE 104)	Leftover Spanish Breakfast Beans (PAGE 114)	Breakfast Fig Smoothie (PAGE 103)
Overnight Breakfast Strata (PAGE 113)	Tuscan Tuna Salad (PAGE 144)	Lemon Chicken Soup (PAGE 128)	Tuna-Stuffed Eggplants (PAGE 142)
Gnocchi with Spinach & Pepper Sauce (PAGE 177)	Portuguese Chorizo Soup (PAGE 201)	Stuffed Baked Squid (PAGE 204)	Saffron Fish Stew with White Beans (PAGE 181)
NOTE: If you have limited time in the mornings, you will want to make tomorrow's breakfast meal tonight so you can simply reheat in the morning. Don't forget to make double the amount of Spanish Breakfast Beans as they will be served twice this week.	**NOTE:** Don't forget to go over this week's goals and action points. Have you noticed your body trying to tell you anything when it comes to the food you eat? Take your time, tune in and start to listen to the messages your body is sending to you.		

WEEK 3

Shopping List

Fruit

- 2 oz. currents
- 4 oz. figs
- 4 oz. fresh figs
- 4 frozen bananas
- 2 lemons
- 4 oz. blueberries
- 4 oz. cherry tomato
- 3 medium tomatoes

Protein

- 4 oz. anchovy fillets
- 4 lb. chicken breasts
- 8 oz. chorizo
- 2 cod fillets
- 1 lb. flounder
- 1 lb. ground beef
- 1 lb. ground pork
- 4 Italian sausages
- 2 lamb racks
- 8 oz. lobster
- 1 lb. prawns
- 2 oz. prosciutto
- 4 salmon fillets
- 8 oz. squid

Vegetables

- 1 lb. arugula
- 2 lb. asparagus
- 3 avocados
- 8 oz. baby sweet peas
- 4 bell peppers
- 8 oz. bulgur wheat
- 1 butternut squash
- 1 lb. carrots
- 1 lb. celery
- 2 oz. chives
- 6 oz. edamame
- 8 oz. green beans
- 1 lb. green onions
- 1 large cabbage
- 1 large cucumber
- 2 lb. lettuce (mixed greens)
- 1 lb. mushrooms
- 2 lb. potatoes
- 1 lb. red onions
- 2 scallions
- 1 lb. spinach
- 2 lb. yellow onions
- 2 lb. zucchini

Pantry

- ½ cup almonds
- ½ cup balsamic vinegar
- 2 qt. beef stock
- 1 cup black olives
- 4 oz. canned green lentils
- 2 oz. capers
- 2 qt. chicken stock
- 8 oz. chickpeas
- 1 cup couscous
- ¼ cup Dijon mustard
- 2 oz. dried apricots
- ½ cup dried cranberries

- ○ 4 oz. flaxseed sprouts
- ○ ½ cup honey
- ○ ½ cup lemon juice
- ○ 4 oz. millet
- ○ 8 oz. oats
- ○ 1 cup olive oil
- ○ 4 oz. pearl barley
- ○ 4 oz. polenta
- ○ ¼ cup prepared mustard
- ○ 6 oz. raisins
- ○ 12 oz. rice
- ○ ½ cup smoked almonds
- ○ 1 cup spelt flour
- ○ 4 oz. sun-dried tomatoes
- ○ ½ cup tahini (sesame paste)
- ○ 1 can tomato paste
- ○ 1 can tomatoes
- ○ 2 cans tuna
- ○ 1 tbsp. vanilla extract
- ○ 2 qt. vegetable stock
- ○ ¼ cup walnuts
- ○ ¼ cup white wine vinegar
- ○ 1 cup whole-wheat flour
- ○ 2 cups whole-wheat gnocchi
- ○ 2 cups whole-wheat orzo pasta
- ○ ¼ cup Worcestershire sauce

Dry Herbs, Spices and Baking

- ○ baking powder
- ○ basil
- ○ bay leaves
- ○ black pepper
- ○ cilantro
- ○ dried marjoram
- ○ dried oregano leaves
- ○ dried porcini mushrooms
- ○ fennel seeds
- ○ garlic powder
- ○ glemon verbena

- ○ mint
- ○ oregano
- ○ paprika
- ○ parsley
- ○ rosemary sprigs
- ○ saffron
- ○ salt
- ○ sugar
- ○ thyme

Dairy

- ○ butter
- ○ cream cheese
- ○ feta cheese
- ○ Greek yogurt
- ○ heavy cream
- ○ Italian ricotta cheese
- ○ milk
- ○ mozzarella cheese
- ○ Parmesan cheese
- ○ ricotta cheese

Bakery and Frozen Items

- ○ bread crumbs
- ○ pie crust
- ○ sourdough bread
- ○ toast
- ○ tortillas

Alcohol Used for Cooking

- ○ Curaçao liqueur
- ○ Madeira wine
- ○ red wine (dry)
- ○ sherry
- ○ white wine

WEEK

Introduction

Welcome to Week 4 of your Mediterranean Meal Plan. This week we are going to discuss food as fuel for our bodies.

When you embark on a new journey of healthy eating, you may come across words such as "micronutrients" and "macronutrients." It's a good idea to become familiar with them and understand what they actually mean, in order to learn what healthy eating is all about and to find a good balance for yourself.

Basically, our body needs nutrients to grow and thrive. Food essentially (and simply) is fuel for our bodies, and it is important that we fill our bodies with the type of fuel it requires.

When we consume food, our bodies convert it into a source we can use. For example, protein is converted into amino acids, which are the building blocks to make muscle, bone, tissue and skin. Healthy fats are needed to maintain good health, create strong healthy cells and support brain function. Carbohydrates are turned into glucose, which supplies our cells with energy, but with too many carbs the excess glucose is stored as fat. Fresh fruits and vegetables support our immune system and provide our bodies with the vitamins and minerals required for good health.

Selecting the Right Foods at Each Meal

Our bodies need the right balance of the right fuel to perform at their best, in the same way that a car needs to be given the appropriate fuel—gas—so it can operate. When selecting the foods (fuel) you consume at each meal, take into consideration the following:

1. Incorporate "living" foods (such as vegetables/fruits/herbs/seeds/spices) into every meal of the day. These will support your overall health and well-being by providing an array of vitamins, minerals and antioxidants. Living foods (mainly vegetables) should make up roughly half your plate.

2. Include a protein portion in every meal of the day. Opt for plant-based protein sources as often as you can; otherwise choose lean varieties of meat, fish or seafood. Quality sources of protein should make up roughly one-quarter of your plate.

3. Look at replacing refined carbohydrates, such as white pasta/white bread, with whole-meal/whole-grain varieties. Whole-meal sources will provide longer-lasting energy as well as greater nutritional value. Complex carbohydrates should make up roughly the other quarter of your plate.

4. Add a serving of a healthy oil/fat to every meal of the day, such as a drizzle of olive oil over a salad or a sprinkle of flaxseeds on top of oatmeal.

Living Foods—The Essential Focus of the Mediterranean Diet

Vegetables, fruits, nuts and seeds are full of vitamins and minerals that make our body work properly, boost our immune system, support normal growth and development, and help cells and organs do their job. Many people today are deficient in an array of nutrients; therefore, it is important that plenty of local, fresh and seasonal fruits and vegetables be incorporated into our daily diet.

Recommendations for daily intake of vitamins and minerals:

1. Eat 5 to 9 handfuls of a wide range of vegetables per day, or as much as possible. Include lots of different colors—for example, mushrooms, cauliflower, bell peppers, tomatoes, leeks, garlic, carrots, etc.

2. Try for two pieces of fruit per day (no more, if you're trying to lose weight). Sample a wide variety of fruits, such as berries, citrus, banana, melons, and so on.

3. Limit fruit at breakfast if you want to lose weight. Choose a high-protein breakfast, which will keep you feeling full for a longer period of time and also balance blood sugar.

4. Buy fruit and vegetables only when in season. Also try to buy local ripe fruit whenever possible—investigate farmer's markets. You will get more nutrients (and flavor) when purchasing in-season, local, ripe produce.

5. Eat raw fruits and vegetables as much as possible. Up to 30% of vitamins can be lost in cooking.

6. Aim to include a bowl of green leafy veggies in your daily diet. Please note lettuce has poor nutritional content so it is better to choose dark leafy greens like spinach, watercress and arugula.

7. Cruciferous vegetables, such as cauliflower, broccoli, cabbage, spinach, kale, bok choy and Brussels sprouts (and similar green leafy vegetables) should be the basis of your veggie intake. These are high in vitamins and soluble fiber and contain many nutrients and phytochemicals that protect against disease. It is thought that cruciferous vegetables are actually better cooked (rather than raw).

8. Potato, pumpkin and sweet potato are high in carbohydrates. Limit your intake unless you have a high exercise level.

9. While nuts and seeds are a good source of protein and fat, they also provide a wide variety of nutrients. Incorporate them into your daily diet—fresh, raw and unsalted. However, watch the amount you consume as they are very high in calories—restrict your intake when you are trying to lose weight.

Final thoughts

Developing a healthy diet calls for choosing a good balance of macro-nutrients such as protein, carbohydrates and healthy fats. We will cover this in greater detail over the following weeks.

Our bodies need the right balance of the right fuel to perform at their best. Selecting the correct foods will help you live an optimized life.

"Living foods" that are bursting with vitamins, minerals and antioxidants are essential for good overall health and well-being. They should make up the largest part of your daily diet.

	SUNDAY	MONDAY	TUESDAY
	Breakfast Fig Smoothie (PAGE 103)	Leftover Neapolitan Polenta Pie (PAGE 199) *(Use leftovers from last night's dinner—simply reheat and serve)*	Caprese Breakfast Tart (PAGE 104)
WEEK 4	Carpaccio (PAGE 130)	Roasted Kale & Chickpea Salad (PAGE 129)	Pickled Herring with Beet Dip Crostini (PAGE 133)
	Neapolitan Polenta Pie (PAGE 199)	Halibut with Lemon-Fennel Salad (PAGE 183)	Caprese Chicken (PAGE 186)

WEDNESDAY	THURSDAY	FRIDAY	SATURDAY
Greek Yogurt Smoothie (PAGE 212)	Breakfast Fig Smoothie (PAGE 103)	Golden Millet Porridge (PAGE 109)	Gourmet Feta Toast (PAGE 110)
Simple Greek Salad (PAGE 131)	Pita Breads with Roasted Lamb & Vegetables (PAGE 134)	Turkey Barley Soup (PAGE 206)	Spinach Torta (PAGE 140)
Meat Loaf Stuffed with Prosciutto & Cheese (PAGE 195)	Fregola with Clams & Chilies (PAGE 194)	Mediterranean Meatballs (PAGE 197)	Mediterranean Baked Cod with Lemon & Garlic (PAGE 147)

WEEK

Shopping List

Vegetables

- 1 lb. arugula
- 2 lb. asparagus
- 3 avocados
- 8 oz. baby sweet peas
- 2 lb. beets
- 4 bell peppers
- 1 butternut squash
- 1 lb. carrots
- 1 lb. celery
- 2 oz. chives
- 8 oz. dried porcini mushrooms
- 2 fennel bulbs
- 8 oz. green beans
- 1 lb. green onions
- 1 lb. kale
- 1 large cabbage
- 1 large cucumber
- 2 lb. lettuce (mixed greens)
- 2 medium eggplants
- 1 lb. mushrooms
- 2 lb. potatoes
- 1 lb. red onions
- 2 scallions
- 1 lb. spinach
- 2 lb. yellow onions
- 2 lb. zucchini

Fruit

- 4 oz. fresh figs
- 4 frozen bananas
- 2 lemons
- 4 oz. cherry tomato
- 3 medium tomatoes
- 2 Nashi pears
- 2 pomegranate arils

Protein

- 1 lb. beef fillet
- 4 lb. chicken breasts
- 8 oz. chorizo
- 1 lb. flounder
- 1 lb. ground beef
- 1 lb. ground pork
- 1 halibut fillet
- 4 Italian sausages
- 2 oz. prosciutto
- 8 oz. squid
- 2 lb. tiny clams or mussels
- 8 oz. turkey breast

Pantry

- ½ cup almonds
- ½ cup balsamic vinegar
- 2 qt. beef stock
- 1 cup black olives
- 4 oz. canned green lentils
- 2 oz. capers
- 2 qt. chicken stock
- 8 oz. chickpeas
- 1 cup couscous
- ¼ cup Dijon mustard
- 2 oz. dried apricots
- ½ cup dried cranberries

- 4 oz. flaxseed sprouts
- ½ cup honey
- ½ cup lemon juice
- 4 oz. millet
- 8 oz. oats
- 1 cup olive oil
- 4 oz. pearl barley
- 4 oz. polenta
- ¼ cup prepared mustard
- 6 oz. raisins
- 12 oz. rice
- ½ cup smoked almonds
- 4 oz. sundried tomatoes
- ½ cup tahini (sesame paste)
- 1 can tomato paste
- 1 can tomatoes
- 2 cans tuna
- 2 qt. vegetable stock
- ¼ cup walnuts
- ¼ cup white wine vinegar
- 1 cup whole-wheat flour
- ¼ cup Worcestershire sauce

Dry Herbs, Spices and Baking Needs

- baking powder
- basil
- bay Leaves
- black pepper
- cilantro
- dried marjoram
- dried oregano leaves
- dried porcini mushrooms
- fennel seeds
- garlic powder
- ground cinnamon

- ground cumin
- Italian dried herbs
- mint
- oregano
- paprika
- parsley
- rosemary sprigs
- saffron
- salt
- sugar
- thyme

Dairy

- butter
- cream cheese
- feta cheese
- Greek yogurt
- heavy cream
- Italian ricotta cheese
- milk
- mozzarella cheese
- Parmesan cheese
- ricotta cheese

Bakery and Frozen Items

- bread crumbs
- pie crust
- toast
- tortillas

Alcohol Used for Cooking

- Curaçao liqueur
- red wine
- white wine

WEEK

5

Introduction

Welcome to Week 5 of your Mediterranean Meal Plan. This week we are placing a spotlight on healthy fats, which are an important focus of the Mediterranean Diet.

Healthy fats (and oils) are an essential part of a healthy diet (one of three macronutrients). They also help with achieving a sense of satiety (keeping us feeling full for a longer period of time) as well as reducing cravings. The Mediterranean Diet features many sources of quality fats such as olives, olive oil, nuts, seeds, avocados and fatty fish.

Since our cell walls are made of both protein and fats, healthy fats and oils play an important role in maintaining good health by helping to keep our cell walls healthy and strong. This is most noticeable with the condition and quality of our skin and hair. Oils also contain vitamins to support our brain and help make it work properly.

The problem many people face is the fact they consume the wrong kind of oils and fats, which can lead to inflammation (as discussed last week) and put them at risk for illness and disease.

Some Leading Sources of Healthy Oils and Fats in the Mediterranean Diet

- Cold-pressed olive oil
- Coconut oil
- Avocado oil
- Macadamia oil
- Flaxseed oil

- Avocados, olives, coconuts, nuts and seeds
- Grass-fed butter and ghee
- Salmon and ground flaxseeds (great sources of omega-3!)

Recommendations for Daily Fats and Oils

- Make sure every meal of the day contains a serving of healthy fats/oils. You can do this by eating half an avocado with breakfast or coconut and ground flaxseeds in a morning smoothie. Lunch could include nuts and seeds in a salad with an olive oil dressing, and at dinnertime you might prepare your meat with either grass-fed ghee or coconut oil, then serve it with a little homemade mayonnaise.

- Aim to include avocados, coconuts, flaxseeds, a variety of nuts and seeds, olives and salmon regularly in your diet.

- Make sure you choose the correct oils to protect from free radicals. Use coconut oil and ghee for food prepared at high heat, and olive oil for medium heat or food served at room temperature. Choose avocado oil, macadamia nut oil and flaxseed oil as dressings to accompany a meal.

- Discontinue any use of toxic man-made oils such as margarine, canola oil and other vegetable oils. These oils are highly inflammatory owing to the way they have been processed/prepared. Always substitute healthier alternatives such as olive oil.

- Reduce the use of animal fats by buying lean cuts of meat. Toxins can be stored in animal fat.

- When cooking, use healthier methods such as steaming, poaching and grilling rather than deep frying.

This Week's Goals

Take note of any man-made oils such as margarine and vegetable oil that you might have already purchased. Are there some you can start replacing with a healthier alternative? Make a list of what you currently own, and once you run out of a less desirable item, try to replace it with a quality, healthier alternative.

Create a list of healthy snacks that are a good source of quality fats. Some ideas includes olives, avocado dip, trail mix and flaxseed crackers. Pick these snacks between meals if you start feeling hungry.

Final Thoughts

Don't forget that the quality fats we have outlined above are not bad for your diet and will not have a negative effect on your health. Instead, they will help combat inflammation, provide long-lasting energy, and give you glowing skin, shiny hair and strong nails. Make "fat" your friend.

	SUNDAY	MONDAY	TUESDAY
	Stuffed Mushrooms (PAGE 115)	Breakfast Fig Smoothie (PAGE 103)	Easy Breakfast Pizza (PAGE 106)
	Tuscan White Bean Stew (PAGE 207)	Chicken Shawarma (PAGE 149)	Traditional Greek Roasted Vegetables (Briam) (PAGE 155)
	Grilled Salmon on Herbed Couscous (PAGE 136)	Tuscan Sausage & Bean Soup (PAGE 145)	Tuna-Stuffed Eggplants (PAGE 142)

WEEK

WEDNESDAY	THURSDAY	FRIDAY	SATURDAY
Plain Greek Yogurt with Fresh Berries (PAGE 225)	Caprese Breakfast Tart (PAGE 104)	Sun Smoothie (PAGE 209)	Lemon Ricotta Pancakes (PAGE 111)
Kofta Kebab (PAGE 157)	Sicilian Eggplant Caponata (PAGE 139)	Authentic Falafel (PAGE 163)	Chickpea Salad (PAGE 223)
Chicken Shawarma (PAGE 149)	Avgolemono Lemon Chicken Soup (PAGE 119)	Moroccan Vegetable Tagine (PAGE 151)	Rosemary Baked Chicken (PAGE 159)

WEEK

5

Shopping List

Fruit

- 4 oz. fresh figs
- 4 frozen bananas
- 2 lemons
- 4 oz. cherry tomato
- 3 medium tomatoes
- 4 oz. raspberries
- 4 oz. strawberries

Protein

- 4 oz. anchovy fillets
- 1 lb. beef fillets
- 4 lb. chicken breasts
- 6 chicken thighs
- 8 oz. chorizo
- 1 lb. flounder
- 1 lb. ground beef
- 1 lb. ground lamb
- 1 lb. ground pork
- 1 halibut fillet
- 4 Italian sausages
- 2 oz. prosciutto
- 8 oz. squid
- 2 lb. tiny clams or mussels
- 8 oz. turkey breast

Vegetables

- 1 lb. arugula
- 2 lb. asparagus
- 3 avocados
- 8 oz. baby sweet peas
- 4 bell peppers
- 1 butternut squash
- 1 lb. carrots
- 1 lb. celery
- 2 oz. chives
- 2 fennel bulbs
- 8 oz. green beans
- 1 lb. green onions
- 1 lb. kale
- 1 large cabbage
- 1 large cucumber
- 2 lb. lettuce (mixed greens)
- 2 medium eggplants
- 1 lb. mushrooms
- 2 lb. potatoes
- 1 lb. red onions
- 2 scallions
- 1 lb. spinach
- 2 lb. sweet potatoes
- 2 lb. yellow onions
- 2 lb. zucchini

Pantry

- ½ cup almonds
- ½ cup balsamic vinegar
- 2 qt. beef stock
- 1 cup black olives
- 4 oz. canned green lentils
- 2 oz. capers
- 2 qt. chicken stock
- 8 oz. chickpeas
- 1 cup couscous
- ¼ cup Dijon mustard
- 2 oz. dried apricots
- ½ cup dried cranberries
- 4 oz. flaxseed sprouts

- ○ ½ cup honey
- ○ ½ cup lemon juice
- ○ 4 oz. millet
- ○ 8 oz. oats
- ○ 1 cup olive oil
- ○ 4 oz. pearl barley
- ○ 4 oz. polenta
- ○ ¼ cup prepared mustard
- ○ 6 oz. raisins
- ○ 12 oz. rice
- ○ ½ cup smoked almonds
- ○ 1 cup spelt flour
- ○ 4 oz. sun-dried tomatoes
- ○ ½ cup tahini (sesame paste)
- ○ 1 can tomato paste
- ○ 1 can tomatoes
- ○ 2 cans tuna
- ○ 1 tbsp. vanilla extract
- ○ 2 qt. vegetable stock
- ○ ¼ cup walnuts
- ○ ¼ cup white wine vinegar
- ○ 1 cup whole-wheat flour
- ○ 2 cups whole-wheat gnocchi
- ○ 2 cups whole-wheat orzo pasta
- ○ ¼ cup Worcestershire sauce

Dry Herbs, Spices and Baking Needs

- ○ baking powder
- ○ basil
- ○ bay leaves
- ○ black pepper
- ○ cilantro
- ○ dried marjoram
- ○ dried oregano leaves
- ○ dried porcini mushrooms
- ○ fennel seed
- ○ garlic powder
- ○ ground cinnamon

- ○ ground cumin
- ○ Italian dried herbs
- ○ lemon verbena
- ○ mint
- ○ oregano
- ○ paprika
- ○ parsley
- ○ rosemary sprigs
- ○ saffron
- ○ salt
- ○ sugar
- ○ thyme

Dairy

- ○ butter
- ○ cream cheese
- ○ feta cheese
- ○ Greek yogurt
- ○ heavy cream
- ○ Italian ricotta cheese
- ○ milk
- ○ mozzarella cheese
- ○ Parmesan cheese
- ○ ricotta cheese

Bakery and Frozen Items

- ○ bread crumbs
- ○ pie crust
- ○ sourdough bread
- ○ toast
- ○ tortillas

Alcohol Used for Cooking

- ○ white wine (dry)

WEEK

6

Introduction

Welcome to Week 6 of your Mediterranean Meal Plan. This week we are taking the time to understand carbohydrates and how to incorporate them into our daily diet in a healthy way.

Carbohydrates provide us with energy through glucose, which is the main fuel for our body. The standard western diet is generally high in carbohydrates, which for some people can present risks such as obesity and type 2 diabetes.

While carbohydrates are an essential part of a healthy diet, don't forget that not all carbs are created equal. It is best to choose healthy carbs with a low glycemic index (GI) such as whole grains, fruits and vegetables. When choosing carbs, we want to also ensure that they have a slow absorption rate—this promotes natural insulin levels rather than drastic insulin spikes. Insulin is the hormone that is essentially used for fat storage. Choosing the wrong carbs as well as consuming a high intake of carbs can contribute dramatically to weight gain.

Some Examples of "Good," Whole Complex Carbs

- Vegetables
- Fruits
- Legumes, such as lentils, chickpeas, kidney beans
- Nuts and seeds
- Whole grains, such as oats, quinoa, brown rice, buckwheat, spelt

Recommendations for Daily Carbohydrate Intake

1. Limit your intake to sources with a low GI and to whole-meal choices such as brown rice, buckwheat, pumpkin and sweet potato.

2. While trying to lose weight, your carb intake should be severely restricted. Serve only small portions as necessary at mealtimes, such as half a potato or ⅓ cup of steamed brown rice.

3. Reduce, as much as possible, your consumption of processed, refined, high-GI carbs such as sugar, refined breads, cakes and pastries, pasta,

sugary drinks and most store-bought breakfast cereals. These foods are low in fiber and provide little nutritional value. They may give you a quick burst of energy at first but will leave you feeling tired and lethargic soon after.

4. Your intake should match your energy output. If you enjoy an active lifestyle and exercise often, you may find you are able to consume a few more carbs than the rest of us. If you are not regularly physically active, your carb intake should be lower.

5. Avoid snacking on "carb foods." Aim for little, light nibbles that contain protein and/or healthy fats such as nuts and seeds, flaxseed crackers, bliss balls made with coconut oil, veggie sticks and hummus.

Final Thoughts

Don't forget there is no "one size fits all" plan when it comes to eating health-fully. This is particularly true when we're talking about consuming carbs. Find what works for you and stick to it—just be sure you are choosing nutrient-rich carbs that that have a low GI and come from whole food sources.

We do suggest, though, that if you are trying to lose weight or may be at risk for type 2 diabetes, you may want to look at limiting the amount of carbs you are serving each mealtime.

	SUNDAY	MONDAY	TUESDAY
	Sun Smoothie (PAGE 209)	Overnight Breakfast Strata (PAGE 113)	Golden Millet Porridge (PAGE 109)
	Lemon Chicken Soup (PAGE 128) *Serve with* Simple Greek Salad (PAGE 131)	Sicilian Eggplant Caponata (PAGE 139)	Rustic Avocado and Corn Salad (PAGE 188)
	Authentic Falafel (PAGE 163)	Falafel Tortillas with Tahini Sauce (PAGE 191)	Chicken Gyro (PAGE 166)

WEEK

NOTES:

To save time, prepare the Caponata today for tomorrow's lunch.

For breakfast tomorrow, you will be serving Overnight Breakfast Strata. As the name suggests, you should make it tonight and store it in the fridge to cook in the morning. Make double the amount for two meals this week.

WEDNESDAY	THURSDAY	FRIDAY	SATURDAY
Tortilla Española (PAGE 116) *(Use chorizo instead of Italian sausage as this will already be on your shopping list this week)*	Golden Millet Porridge (PAGE 109)	Cottage Cheese Blueberry Casserole (PAGE 105)	Caprese Breakfast Tart (PAGE 104)
Watermelon & Mint Salad (PAGE 126)	Portuguese Chorizo Soup (PAGE 201)	Shrimp & Asparagus Salad (PAGE 138)	Carpaccio (PAGE 130)
Sweet Baked Meatballs (Soutzoukakia) (PAGE 167)	Traditional Olives & Feta Salad (PAGE 127)	Mediterranean Meatballs (PAGE 197)	Fish in Island Sauce (PAGE 193)
			NOTE: You made it! It's Saturday so grab yourself a glass of wine or two and a square of dark chocolate.

WEEK 6

Shopping List

Vegetables

- 1 lb. arugula
- 2 lb. asparagus
- 8 oz. baby sweet peas
- 4 bell peppers
- 1 butternut squash
- 1 lb. carrots
- 1 lb. celery
- 2 oz. chives
- 8 oz. green beans
- 1 lb. green onions
- 1 large cabbage
- 1 large cucumber
- 2 lb. lettuce (mixed greens)
- 2 medium eggplants
- 1 lb. mushrooms
- 2 lb. potatoes
- 1 lb. red onions
- 2 scallions
- 1 small watermelon
- 1 lb. spinach
- 2 lb. yellow onions
- 2 lb. zucchini

Fruit

- 4 oz. fresh figs
- 4 frozen bananas
- 2 lemons
- 4 oz. cherry tomato
- 3 medium tomatoes
- 1 small clam raspberries
- 1 small clam strawberries

Protein

- 4 oz. anchovy fillets
- 1 lb. beef fillet
- 4 lb. chicken breasts
- 6 chicken thighs
- 8 oz. chorizo
- 1 lb. ground beef
- 1 lb. ground lamb
- 1 lb. ground pork
- 1 halibut fillet
- 4 Italian sausages
- 8 oz. shrimp
- 8 oz. turkey breast

Pantry

- ½ cup balsamic vinegar
- 2 qt. beef stock
- 1 cup black olives
- 4 oz. canned green lentils
- 2 oz. capers
- 2 qt. chicken stock
- 8 oz. chickpeas
- 1 cup couscous
- ¼ cup Dijon mustard
- 2 oz. dried apricots
- ½ cup dried cranberries
- 4 oz. flaxseed sprouts
- ½ cup honey

- ○ ½ cup lemon juice
- ○ 4 oz. millet
- ○ 8 oz. oats
- ○ 1 cup olive oil
- ○ 4 oz. pearl barley
- ○ 4 oz. polenta
- ○ ¼ cup prepared mustard
- ○ 6 oz. raisins
- ○ 12 oz. rice
- ○ ½ cup smoked almonds
- ○ 1 cup spelt flour
- ○ 4 oz. sun-dried tomatoes
- ○ ½ cup tahini (sesame paste)
- ○ 1 can tomato paste
- ○ 1 can tomatoes
- ○ 2 cans tuna
- ○ 1 tbsp. vanilla extract
- ○ 2 qt. vegetable stock
- ○ ¼ cup walnuts
- ○ ¼ cup white wine vinegar
- ○ 1 cup whole-wheat flour
- ○ 2 cups whole-wheat gnocchi
- ○ 2 cups whole-wheat orzo pasta
- ○ ¼ cup Worcestershire sauce

Dry Herbs, Spices and Baking Needs

- ○ baking powder
- ○ basil
- ○ bay leaves
- ○ black pepper
- ○ cilantro
- ○ dried marjoram
- ○ dried oregano leaves
- ○ dried porcini mushrooms

- ○ fennel seeds
- ○ garlic powder
- ○ ground cinnamon
- ○ ground cumin
- ○ Italian dried herbs
- ○ lemon verbena
- ○ mint
- ○ oregano
- ○ paprika
- ○ parsley
- ○ rosemary sprigs
- ○ saffron
- ○ salt
- ○ sugar
- ○ thyme

Dairy

- ○ butter
- ○ cream cheese
- ○ feta cheese
- ○ Greek yogurt
- ○ heavy cream
- ○ Italian Ricotta
- ○ milk
- ○ mozzarella cheese
- ○ Parmesan cheese
- ○ ricotta cheese

Bakery and Frozen Items

- ○ bread crumbs
- ○ pie crust
- ○ sourdough bread
- ○ toast
- ○ tortillas

WEEK

7

Introduction

Welcome to Week 7 of your Mediterranean Meal Plan. This week we are looking at protein, another macronutrient like carbohydrates and fats.

Protein is an important part of a healthy diet. Studies have actually shown that protein can help improve health in many ways, including lowering blood pressure and combating diabetes as well as achieving weight loss and improving strength. We want to make sure we are consuming a high-quality source of protein at each mealtime.

Protein is a nutrient that is converted into amino acids. These are the body's building blocks for muscle, bone, tissue and skin. We also need amino acids to make enzymes, hormones and even our DNA. Our body does not store a lot of protein, so we must constantly replace it by consuming it in our diet. Many people today do not provide enough protein in their diet while at the same time getting too many calories from sugar and carbs. If we do not have enough protein in our diet, we start to break down muscle to make up for the loss.

Some Sources of Dietary Protein

- Beans and legumes (such as lentils and chickpeas)
- Lean meat, poultry, fish and seafood
- Eggs
- Dairy products like milk, yogurt and cheese
- Seeds and nuts

Recommendations for Daily Protein Intake

1. Make sure you serve at least one helping of good quality protein each day from lean chicken, fish or free-range eggs.

2. Remember to see that most sources of protein are vegetable based. Lentils, beans, chickpeas, quinoa and chia are all good options. Aim for at least one meatless day each week, but work toward 3 to 4 days where your main focus will be on plant-based protein sources. This will give your digestive system a rest, which in turn will support your overall state of health.

3. Limit red meat to only once or twice per week. Choose lean cuts from wild sources when possible. Red meat is very acidic and can upset the body's alkaline environment. A highly acidic diet can also contribute to fatigue, compromise the immune system and make us vulnerable to illness.

4. Make sure a serving of protein is present in every meal each day, such as eggs or natural Greek yogurt for breakfast; nuts, seeds and feta cheese crumbled in a salad for lunch; and legumes/beans or lean meat for dinner.

Final Thoughts

Protein will help support a healthy diet. It can enable you to keep off unwanted weight, reduce the risks associated with type 2 diabetes—or help you avoid it altogether—and assist in controlling blood pressure.

It is important to use lean, quality sources of protein and focus particularly on plant-based varieties to ensure you are reaping the full rewards and health benefits that this amazing nutrient has to offer.

SUNDAY	MONDAY	TUESDAY	
Spanish Breakfast Beans (PAGE 114) *(Make double the amount required to serve as leftovers for Tuesday's breakfast)	Plain Greek Yogurt & Fresh Berries (PAGE 225)	Spanish Breakfast Beans (PAGE 114) *(Use Sunday's leftovers)	
Chicken Gyro (PAGE 160)	Tuscan Tuna Salad (PAGE 144)	Caprese Chicken (PAGE 186)	
Chicken Piccata (PAGE 189)	Seafood Paella (PAGE 153)	Sicilian Eggplant Caponata (PAGE 139)	

WEDNESDAY	THURSDAY	FRIDAY	SATURDAY
Gourmet Feta Toast (PAGE 110)	Cottage Cheese Blueberry Casserole (PAGE 105) *(Make two full servings to have enough for breakfast on Saturday)*	Sun Smoothie (PAGE 209)	Cottage Cheese Blueberry Casserole (PAGE 105) *(Use the leftovers from Thursday)*
Authentic Falafel (PAGE 163)	Turkey Barley Soup (PAGE 206) *(Use the leftovers from last night's dinner)*	Grilled Salmon with Tomato-Avocado Salsa (PAGE 172)	Grilled Heirloom Tomato & Feta Panzanella (PAGE 174)
Turkey Barley Soup (PAGE 206) *(Make a larger portion that can be reused over the coming days)*	Spinach Torta (PAGE 140)	Shakshuka with Tomato Sauce & Pepper (PAGE 165)	Tuscan White Bean Stew (PAGE 207)
NOTE: Prep the Cottage Cheese Casserole tonight for tomorrow's breakfast to save time in the morning.			

WEEK

7

Shopping List

Vegetables

- 1 lb. arugula
- 2 lb. asparagus
- 3 avocados
- 8 oz. baby sweet peas
- 4 bell peppers
- 1 butternut squash
- 1 lb. carrots
- 1 lb. celery
- 2 oz. chives
- 2 fennel bulbs
- 8 oz. green beans
- 1 lb. green onions
- 1 lb. kale
- 1 large cabbage
- 1 large cucumber
- 2 lb. lettuce (mixed greens)
- 2 medium eggplants
- 3 medium pickles
- 1 lb. mushrooms
- 2 lb. potatoes
- 1 lb. red onions
- 2 scallions
- 1 lb. spinach
- 2 lb. sweet potatoes
- 2 lb. yellow onions
- 2 lb. zucchini

Fruit

- 4 oz. fresh figs
- 4 frozen bananas
- 2 lemons
- 4 oz. cherry tomato
- 3 medium tomatoes
- 4 oz. raspberries
- 4 oz. strawberries

Protein

- 4 lb. chicken breasts
- 4 eggs
- 2 fish fillets
- 1 lb. lobster
- 4 oz. prosciutto
- 2 salmon fillets
- 8 oz. shrimp
- 1 lb. tiny clams
- 8 oz. turkey breast

Pantry

- ½ cup almonds
- ½ cup balsamic vinegar
- 2 qt. beef stock
- 1 cup black olives
- 4 oz. canned green lentils
- 2 oz. capers
- 2 qt. chicken stock
- 8 oz. chickpeas
- 1 cup couscous
- ¼ cup Dijon mustard
- 2 oz. dried apricots
- ½ cup dried cranberries
- 4 oz. flaxseed sprouts

- ½ cup honey
- ½ cup lemon juice
- 4 oz. millet
- 8 oz. oats
- 1 cup olive oil
- 1 cup orange juice
- ½ cup pearl barley
- 4 oz. polenta
- ¼ cup prepared mustard
- 6 oz. raisins
- 12 oz. rice
- ½ cup smoked almonds
- 1 cup spelt flour
- 4 oz. sun-dried tomatoes
- ½ cup tahini (sesame paste)
- 1 can tomato paste
- 1 can tomatoes
- 2 cans tuna
- 1 tbsp. vanilla extract
- 2 qt. vegetable stock
- ¼ cup walnuts
- ¼ cup white wine vinegar
- 1 cup whole-wheat flour
- 2 cups whole-wheat gnocchi
- 2 cups whole-wheat orzo pasta
- ¼ cup Worcestershire sauce

Dry Herbs, Spices and Baking Needs

- baking powder
- basil
- bay leaf
- black pepper
- cilantro
- dried marjoram
- dried oregano leaves
- dried porcini mushrooms
- fennel seeds

- garlic powder
- ground cinnamon
- ground cumin
- Italian dried herbs
- lemon verbena
- mint
- oregano
- paprika
- parsley
- rosemary sprigs
- saffron
- salt
- sugar
- thyme

Dairy

- butter
- cream cheese
- feta cheese
- Greek yogurt
- heavy cream
- Italian ricotta cheese
- milk
- mozzarella cheese
- Parmesan cheese
- ricotta cheese

Bakery

- crusty bread
- French bread
- pie crust
- sheet puff pastry

Alcohol Used for Cooking

- white wine

WEEK

8

Introduction

Congratulations!

You've made it to week 8 and you're heading down the home stretch!

You now have the information required to reach your health goals and maintain a way of eating that will help ensure your success.

This program has kick-started your way to a life of greater vitality and longevity. You now have acquired the skills to knowing what foods to select to make sure you are eating for optimal health, create daily healthy habits and learn to listen to and be in tune with your body.

You may have experienced weight loss, increased energy, clearer skin and enjoyed other health benefits due to excising empty and inflammatory items from your diet and following a diet rich in the macronutrients that your body needs. The long-term benefits of these are significant, and now you can look forward to an enhanced quality of life.

Steps Ahead

Feel free to continue to use this program as a guide to carry on with the same enhanced eating habits. You will now notice that the meals each week share a number of similarities. This will be the basis of your healthy eating from now on, and you can continue eating this way indefinitely. Let's quickly recap some of the basics to remember for everyday healthy eating from here on in:

- Have fun! Healthy eating is meant to be enjoyable, exciting and simple. There is no need to stress about it or make things overly complicated. Take note of what you have on hand each week and make use of what recommended ingredients are available to plan your menus.

- Make "whole food" swaps with the things you can easily make. Don't forget to pay attention to the ingredients list on packaged food items so you can make sure you're investing in the best possible foods for your health.

- Prepare what you can ahead of time to take the stress and chaos out of rushing things at mealtimes. Don't forget that food is not your enemy—it's fuel for your mind and body.

- Choosing the right foods will significantly reduce your risk of illness and chronic disease while helping you feel great at the same time! Consistently picking foods, on the other hand, that trigger negative responses (don't forget, your body will tell you which ones those are) can accelerate inflammatory processes, leaving you susceptible to disease.

- Our body needs the right balance of the proper fuels to perform at its best. Selecting the correct foods will set you on the path to an optimized life.

- Picking foods that are bursting with vitamins, minerals and antioxidants is essential for overall health and well-being. These foods should make up the greater part of your daily diet.

- Don't forget: quality fats are not bad for you and will not have a negative effect on your health. Instead, they can help combat inflammation, provide long-lasting energy and give you glowing skin, shiny hair and strong nails. Make "fat" your friend.

- There is no "one size fits all" plan when it comes to eating healthfully—particularly when it's a question of consuming carbs. Be sure to choose nutrient-rich carbs that are low in GI and come from whole food sources.

- Lean, quality protein sources (in particular plant-based varieties) will help support a healthy diet. Protein can enable you to keep off unwanted weight, reduce the risks associated with type 2 diabetes and help you manage blood pressure.

Final Thoughts

The occasional treat is ok—great, in fact, if you want to nourish your soul and ensure a healthy relationship with food. A good rule of thumb is to practice the 80/20 principle. According to this principle, you should choose foods that nurture and nourish your *body* 80% of the time, while allowing yourself to enjoy the foods that nurture and nourish your *soul* 20% of the time.

Don't forget this program is designed to teach you how food affects your overall health. If you fall back on old unhealthy habits, you will be sure to lose the positive effects of healthy eating that you have gone to so much effort up till now to achieve.

SUNDAY	MONDAY	TUESDAY
Golden Millet Porridge (PAGE 109)	Easy Breakfast Pizza (PAGE 106)	Fruit Salad with Italian Ricotta (PAGE 108)
Turkey Barley Soup (PAGE 206)	Carpaccio (PAGE 130)	Chickpea Salad (PAGE 223)
Mediterranean Meatballs (PAGE 197)	Shrimp & Leek Spaghetti (PAGE 169)	Panko Salmon with Snap Peas (PAGE 170)

WEEK

WEDNESDAY	THURSDAY	FRIDAY	SATURDAY
Lemon Ricotta Pancakes (PAGE 111)	Golden Millet Porridge (PAGE 109)	Breakfast Fig Smoothie (PAGE 103)	Stuffed Mushrooms (PAGE 115)
Chicken Souvlaki with Tzatziki (PAGE 120)	Zesty Lemon Rice (PAGE 123)	Chicken & Bulgur Salad with Peaches (PAGE 178)	Beef Kofta Patties with Cucumber Salad (PAGE 182)
Pasta Salad with Tomatoes & Eggplant (PAGE 173)	Turkey Barley Soup (PAGE 206)	Rustic Avocado and Corn Salad topped with Caprese Chicken (PAGE 188) & (PAGE 186)	Almond-Crusted Trout with Swiss Chard (PAGE 179)

NOTES:

WOW! You've completed the full 8-week challenge! Start planning your 9th week (and all weeks afterward) with some of your favorite recipes that you've tried over the past 8 weeks.

Don't forget to have a couple of glasses of really special wine tonight to celebrate!

WEEK

8

Shopping List

○ 1 lb. spinach
○ 2 lb. yellow onions
○ 2 lb. zucchini

Fruit

○ 2 apples
○ 4 oz. fresh figs
○ 4 frozen bananas
○ 2 lemons
○ 4 oz. cherry tomato
○ 3 medium tomatoes
○ 2 Nashi pears
○ 4 oz. raspberries
○ 4 oz. strawberries

Vegetables

○ 2 apples
○ 1 lb. arugula
○ 2 lb. asparagus
○ 3 avocados
○ 8 oz. baby sweet peas
○ 4 bell peppers
○ 1 butternut squash
○ 1 lb. carrots
○ 1 lb. celery
○ 2 oz. chives
○ 2 fennel bulbs
○ 8 oz. green beans
○ 1 lb. green onions
○ 1 lb. kale
○ 1 large cabbage
○ 1 large cucumber
○ 2 leeks
○ 3 lemons
○ 2 lb. lettuce (mixed greens)
○ 2 medium eggplants
○ 1 lb. mushrooms
○ 2 lb. potatoes
○ 1 lb. red onions
○ 2 scallions

Protein

○ 1 lb. beef fillet
○ 4 lb. chicken breasts
○ 4 eggs
○ 1 lb. ground beef
○ 1 lb. ground sirloin
○ 4 oz. prosciutto
○ 2 salmon fillets
○ 8 oz. shrimp
○ 1 lb. tiny clams
○ 2 trout fillets
○ 8 oz. turkey breast

Pantry

○ ½ cup balsamic vinegar
○ 2 qt. beef stock
○ 1 cup black olives
○ 4 oz. canned green lentils
○ 2 oz. capers
○ 2 qt. chicken stock
○ 8 oz. chickpeas
○ 1 cup couscous
○ ¼ cup Dijon mustard
○ 2 oz. dried apricots

- ½ cup dried cranberries
- 4 oz. flaxseed sprouts
- ½ cup honey
- ½ cup lemon juice
- 4 oz. millet
- 8 oz. oats
- 1 cup olive oil
- 1 cup orange juice
- 4 oz. pearl barley
- 4 oz. polenta
- ¼ cup prepared mustard
- ½ cup raisins
- 12 oz. rice
- ½ cup smoked almonds
- 1 cup spelt flour
- 4 oz. sun-dried tomatoes
- ½ cup tahini (sesame paste)
- 1 can tomato paste
- 1 can tomatoes
- 2 cans tuna
- 1 tbsp. vanilla extract
- 2 qt. vegetable stock
- ¼ cup walnuts
- ¼ cup white wine vinegar
- 1 cup whole-wheat flour
- 2 cups whole-wheat gnocchi
- 2 cups whole-wheat orzo pasta
- ¼ cup Worcestershire sauce

Dry Herbs, Spices and Baking Needs

- baking powder
- basil
- bay leaves
- black pepper
- cilantro
- dried marjoram
- dried oregano leaves

- dried porcini mushrooms
- fennel seeds
- garlic powder
- lemon verbena
- mint
- oregano
- paprika
- parsley
- rosemary sprigs
- saffron
- salt
- sugar
- thyme

Dairy

- butter
- cream cheese
- feta cheese
- Greek yogurt
- heavy cream
- Italian ricotta
- milk
- mozzarella cheese
- Parmesan cheese
- ricotta cheese

Bakery

- crusty bread
- French bread
- pie crust
- sheet puff pastry

Alcohol Used for Cooking

- ½ cup red wine
- ½ cup white wine

RECIPES

Breakfast
RECIPES

Breakfast Fig Smoothie

Serves: 2

INGREDIENTS

4 large fresh figs, cut into quarters

2 small/medium frozen bananas, sliced

¼ cup natural Greek yogurt

3 tbsp. oats

3 tbsp. almonds

2 tbsp. honey

1 tbsp. chia seeds

1 cup water

1 cup ice

INSTRUCTIONS

1. Combine all the ingredients in a high-speed blender and process on high for 1 minute or until smooth. Add more liquid if necessary to adjust thickness, and blend again.

2. Divide between two tall glasses and serve immediately.

NUTRITION · DATA FOR 1 SERVING:

Calories **470kcal**	Sodium **41mg**
Total Carbohydrates **81g**	Potassium **915mg**
Protein **11g**	Dietary Fiber **12g**
Total Fat **15g**	Sugars **57g**
Saturated Fat **2g**	Vitamin A **6% Daily Value**
Polyunsaturated Fat **3g**	Vitamin C **19% Daily Value**
Monounsaturated Fat **7g**	Calcium **51% Daily Value**
Trans Fat **0g**	Iron **14% Daily Value**
Cholesterol **3mg**	

Caprese Breakfast Tart

Serves: 8

INGREDIENTS

1 large sheet puff pastry

2 tbsp. olive oil

36 thin slices tomato

36 thin slices fresh buffalo-milk mozzarella

¼ cup freshly grated Parmesan cheese

¼ cup torn fresh basil leaves

INSTRUCTIONS

1. Preheat the oven to 425°F. Line a baking sheet with nonstick paper.

2. Lay the puff pastry sheet out flat on the lined baking sheet. Lightly brush the pastry with 1 tablespoon of the olive oil throughout.

3. Place three rows of 12 tomato slices and 12 mozzarella cheese slices on the pastry, alternating as you go and overlapping slightly, ensuring you leave a ½-inch to 1-inch border around all sides.

4. Once all three rows are arranged, drizzle over the remaining tablespoon of olive oil and sprinkle with the Parmesan cheese.

5. Bake 30–35 minutes or until golden.

6. Remove from the oven and sprinkle with the fresh basil leaves. Slice and serve immediately.

NUTRITION · DATA FOR 1 SERVING:

Calories **377kcal**	Sodium **190mg**
Total Carbohydrates **17g**	Potassium **191mg**
Protein **19g**	Dietary Fiber **1g**
Total Fat **28g**	Sugars **2g**
Saturated Fat **9g**	Vitamin A **15% Daily Value**
Polyunsaturated Fat **7g**	Vitamin C **15% Daily Value**
Monounsaturated Fat **6g**	Calcium **24% Daily Value**
Trans Fat **0g**	Iron **6% Daily Value**
Cholesterol **40mg**	

Cottage Cheese Blueberry Casserole

Serves: 6

INGREDIENTS

4 eggs, separated

⅔ cup monk fruit sweetener (or natural sugar of choice)

⅔ cup flour, sifted

2 tbsp. freshly squeezed lemon juice

2 tsp. finely grated lemon peel

1 tsp. vanilla extract

1 tsp. almond extract

½ tsp. salt

2 cups cottage cheese

1 cup sour cream

1½ cups fresh blueberries

INSTRUCTIONS

1. Preheat the oven to 300°F and lightly grease an 8-inch casserole dish. Set aside.

2. In a medium bowl, beat the egg yolks until light. Blend in the sweetener, spelt flour, lemon juice, lemon peel, vanilla, almond extract, and salt.

3. Place the cottage cheese into a large bowl, then add a small amount of the egg yolk mixture and beat on high speed until the curds are broken and the mixture is nearly smooth.

4. Add the remaining egg yolk mixture and the sour cream. Beat until blended.

5. In a separate bowl, beat the egg whites until stiff but not dry, then fold into the cheese mixture.

6. Pour into the greased casserole dish. Place in the oven and bake for 40 minutes.

7. Remove from the oven and sprinkle the blueberries on top in an even layer. Continue to bake for another 20 minutes. Refrigerate at least 5hours before serving.

NUTRITION · DATA FOR 1 SERVING:

Calories **244kcal**	Sodium **542mg**
Total Carbohydrates **41g**	Potassium **134mg**
Protein **18g**	Dietary Fiber **2g**
Total Fat **10g**	Sugars **29g**
Saturated Fat **6g**	Vitamin A **11% Daily Value**
Polyunsaturated Fat **1g**	Vitamin C **9% Daily Value**
Monounsaturated Fat **2g**	Calcium **11% Daily Value**
Trans Fat **0.6g**	Iron **8% Daily Value**
Cholesterol **165mg**	

Easy Breakfast Pizza

Serves: 4

INGREDIENTS

1½ cups self-rising flour, plus more for kneading

1 cup plain Greek yogurt

2 tbsp. olive oil

½ cup arugula leaves

⅓ cup sliced mushrooms

¼ cup cream cheese

5 slices prosciutto, chopped

3 eggs

⅓ cup freshly grated Parmesan cheese

salt and pepper, to taste

INSTRUCTIONS

1. Preheat the oven to 450°F. Lightly grease a 12-inch pizza pan.

2. In a mixing bowl, mix together the flour and the yogurt, using your hands if necessary.

3. Tip out onto a floured flat surface and knead together for approximately 10 minutes, adding more flour as necessary to prevent from sticking.

4. Place the dough on the prepared pan and, starting from the center, spread it to the edges of the pan.

5. Bake for 6 minutes, until the base just begins to brown, then remove from the oven.

6. Spread the olive oil over the crust, then sprinkle with the arugula and mushrooms.

7. Drop dollops of the cream cheese one teaspoon at a time over the top of the pizza, then arrange the prosciutto in an even fashion on the top.

NUTRITION · DATA FOR 1 SERVING:

Calories **428kcal**	Sodium **1142mg**
Total Carbohydrates **40g**	Potassium **335mg**
Protein **19g**	Dietary Fiber **1g**
Total Fat **21g**	Sugars **5g**
Saturated Fat **8g**	Vitamin A **9% Daily Value**
Polyunsaturated Fat **2g**	Vitamin C **1% Daily Value**
Monounsaturated Fat **9g**	Calcium **39% Daily Value**
Trans Fat **2.3g**	Iron **17% Daily Value**
Cholesterol **174mg**	

8. Carefully crack the eggs on top of the pizza, toward the center so they do not run off the edge. Sprinkle with Parmesan cheese and a good crack of salt and pepper.

9. Bake for an additional 10 to 15 minutes or until the toppings are thoroughly heated, the eggs are cooked to your liking and the crust is a deep golden brown. Slice and serve immediately.

Fruit Salad with Italian Ricotta

Serves: 6

INGREDIENTS

2 large apples, cored and thinly sliced

2 large Nashi pears, cored and thinly sliced

1 cup fresh baby spinach leaves

⅓ cup dried cranberries

⅓ cup finely chopped walnuts

⅔ cup Italian ricotta

2½ tbsp. raw honey

½ tbsp. freshly squeezed lemon juice

½ tsp. ground cinnamon

INSTRUCTIONS

1. In a salad bowl, toss together the apples, pears, spinach, dried cranberries and walnuts.

2. In a separate bowl, whip together the Italian ricotta, honey, lemon juice and cinnamon. Add to the fruit mixture and toss to combine. Serve immediately.

NUTRITION · DATA FOR 1 SERVING:

Calories **309kcal**	Sodium **125mg**
Total Carbohydrates **27g**	Potassium **295mg**
Protein **15g**	Dietary Fiber **3g**
Total Fat **17g**	Sugars **16g**
Saturated Fat **8g**	Vitamin A **17% Daily Value**
Polyunsaturated Fat **4g**	Vitamin C **10% Daily Value**
Monounsaturated Fat **4g**	Calcium **30% Daily Value**
Trans Fat **1.7g**	Iron **5% Daily Value**
Cholesterol **48mg**	

Golden Millet Porridge

Serves: 4

INGREDIENTS

For the porridge:
1½ cups millet, uncooked

½ cup diced apple

½ cup diced butternut squash

3 cups milk of choice

2 cups water

½ tsp. ground cinnamon

¼ tsp. sea salt

To serve:
2 tbsp. honey

¼ cup roughly chopped walnuts

¼ cup raisins

1 pinch ground cinnamon

INSTRUCTIONS

1. Combine all the porridge ingredients in a large saucepan and bring to a boil over low-medium heat.

2. Cover and reduce the heat, then allow to simmer until the liquid is absorbed, and the millet, squash and apple are tender, approximately 25 minutes.

3. To serve, divide the porridge among serving bowls. Drizzle with a little honey, a sprinkle of walnuts and raisins and a pinch of ground cinnamon. Feel free to also add a dash of milk if you wish.

NUTRITION · DATA FOR 1 SERVING:

Calories **512kcal**	Sodium **226mg**
Total Carbohydrates **83g**	Potassium **539mg**
Protein **16g**	Dietary Fiber **8g**
Total Fat **14g**	Sugars **24g**
Saturated Fat **4g**	Vitamin A **32% Daily Value**
Polyunsaturated Fat **6g**	Vitamin C **8% Daily Value**
Monounsaturated Fat **3g**	Calcium **24% Daily Value**
Trans Fat **1.4g**	Iron **15% Daily Value**
Cholesterol **18 mg**	

Gourmet Feta Toast

Serves: 2

INGREDIENTS

4 slices toast of choice
(rye/sourdough/
multigrain)

½ cup soft Greek feta
cheese

2 small tomatoes,
thinly sliced

1 avocado, thinly sliced

¼ cup pomegranate
ariels

2 tbsp. pepitas

2 tbsp. flaxseed sprouts
(optional)

4 lemon (or lime)
wedges

INSTRUCTIONS

1. Prepare your toast according to your liking.
Once done, transfer the slices to serving plates.

2. Spread each slice of toast with the feta cheese.
Top with the slices of tomato and avocado, then
sprinkle over the pomegranate ariels, pepitas and
flaxseed sprouts, if using.

3. Serve immediately with a lemon or lime wedge
to squeeze over the top.

NUTRITION · DATA FOR 1 SERVING:

Calories **223kcal**	Sodium **318mg**
Total Carbohydrates **22g**	Potassium **372mg**
Protein **7g**	Dietary Fiber **5g**
Total Fat **12g**	Sugars **3g**
Saturated Fat **3g**	Vitamin A **12% Daily Value**
Polyunsaturated Fat **2g**	Vitamin C **26% Daily Value**
Monounsaturated Fat **6g**	Calcium **5% Daily Value**
Trans Fat **0.3g**	Iron **8% Daily Value**
Cholesterol **11mg**	

Lemon Ricotta Pancakes

Serves: 3 (about 6 large pancakes)

INGREDIENTS

⅔ cup ricotta cheese

2 large eggs, separated

¼ cup milk of choice

¼ cup, plus 2 tbsp. whole-wheat flour

2 tsp. sugar

¼ tsp. baking powder

⅛ tsp. salt

1 tbsp. finely minced lemon peel

1 tsp. finely minced lemon verbena

2 tsp. olive oil

INSTRUCTIONS

1. The night before, place the cheese in a piece of cheesecloth or a paper coffee filter and set in a strainer over a bowl. Cover with plastic wrap and refrigerate. In the morning, discard the whey collected in the bowl.

2. Transfer the drained ricotta to a food processor or blender, add the egg yolks and process until smooth.

3. Add the milk, flour, sugar, baking powder and salt and process until completely blended.

4. Fold in the lemon peel and lemon verbena.

5. Beat the egg whites in a mixing bowl until just stiff but still moist, then fold gently into the batter.

6. Heat the olive oil in a large nonstick skillet over medium heat. Drop the batter by ¼ cupfuls onto the skillet and cook until the tops bubble. Turn and cook on the second side until golden brown.

recipe continues

NUTRITION · DATA FOR 1 SERVING:

Calories **135kcal**	Sodium **122mg**
Total Carbohydrates **11g**	Potassium **79mg**
Protein **6g**	Dietary Fiber **1g**
Total Fat **8g**	Sugars **3g**
Saturated Fat **3g**	Vitamin A **6% Daily Value**
Polyunsaturated Fat **0.5g**	Vitamin C **2% Daily Value**
Monounsaturated Fat **2g**	Calcium **10% Daily Value**
Trans Fat **2g**	Iron **4% Daily Value**
Cholesterol **89mg**	

7. Repeat with the remaining batter.

8. Serve immediately with your favorite toppings, such as lemon juice with a dusting of sugar or a drizzle of fresh local honey.

Overnight Breakfast Strata

Serves: 6

INGREDIENTS

12 slices sourdough bread, cubed

1 lb. ground pork

⅓ cup chopped onion

⅓ cup chopped green pepper

1 (4-oz.) jar pimientos, drained and chopped

6 large eggs

3 cups milk

½ cup cubed feta cheese

2 tsp. Worcestershire sauce

2 tsp. fresh oregano

1 tsp. ground mustard

½ tsp. sea salt

¼ tsp. pepper

INSTRUCTIONS

1. Lightly grease a 9-by-13-inch baking pan or casserole dish and spread in the bread cubes; set aside.

2. In a skillet over medium heat, combine the ground pork, onion and green pepper. Cook until the pork is browned, then drain off any excess fat.

3. Stir in the pimientos, then sprinkle the pork and vegetable mixture over the bread.

4. In a bowl, beat together the eggs, milk, feta cheese, Worcestershire sauce, oregano, mustard, salt and pepper and carefully pour over the pork mixture. Cover and refrigerate overnight.

5. The next day, remove the strata from the fridge and allow to come to room temperature.

6. Preheat the oven to 325°F.

7. Bake, covered, for 1 hour and 20 minutes.

8. Uncover and bake 10 minutes longer or until a knife inserted near the center comes out clean.

9. Let stand for 10 minutes before serving.

NUTRITION · DATA FOR 1 SERVING:

Calories **426kcal**	Sodium **695mg**
Total Carbohydrates **42g**	Potassium **349mg**
Protein **20g**	Dietary Fiber **1g**
Total Fat **17g**	Sugars **6g**
Saturated Fat **8g**	Vitamin A **11% Daily Value**
Polyunsaturated Fat **1g**	Vitamin C **33% Daily Value**
Monounsaturated Fat **7g**	Calcium **16% Daily Value**
Trans Fat **0.9g**	Iron **16% Daily Value**
Cholesterol **57mg**	

Spanish Breakfast Beans

Serves: 4

INGREDIENTS

2 cups chicken or vegetable stock

1 small potato, diced

½ medium bell pepper, seeded and finely diced

1½ tsp. garlic powder

2 tbsp. sofrito

1 tsp. sazon, or a little more, to taste

3 tbsp. tomato sauce

1 (14-oz.) can pinto beans

To serve:
freshly squeezed lemon juice, to taste

salt and pepper, to taste

crusty bread or toast

INSTRUCTIONS

1. Combine all the ingredients in a medium saucepan over medium heat. Boil until the vegetables are tender and cooked through, approximately 20 minutes.

2. Season with a squeeze of lemon juice and salt and black pepper, to taste.

3. Serve over or alongside crusty bread or toast if desired.

NUTRITION · DATA FOR 1 SERVING:

Calories **150kcal**	Sodium **697mg**
Total Carbohydrates **23g**	Potassium **306mg**
Protein **7g**	Dietary Fiber **6g**
Total Fat **2g**	Sugars **4g**
Saturated Fat **0g**	Vitamin A **15% Daily Value**
Polyunsaturated Fat **0.1g**	Vitamin C **66% Daily Value**
Monounsaturated Fat **0g**	Calcium **5% Daily Value**
Trans Fat **2g**	Iron **10% Daily Value**
Cholesterol **0mg**	

Stuffed Mushrooms

Serves: 4

INGREDIENTS

8 large portobello mushrooms

6 tbsp. extra-virgin olive oil

1 onion, finely diced

1 clove garlic, minced

1 zucchini, finely diced

1 bell pepper, seeded and finely diced

2 tomatoes, finely diced

3 tbsp. chopped fresh chives

½ tbsp. freshly squeezed lemon juice

salt and pepper, to taste

INSTRUCTIONS

1. Preheat the oven to 350°F.

2. Wipe the mushrooms clean and remove their stems (save for another use).

3. Lightly cover a baking sheet with 2 tablespoons of the oil and set the mushrooms on the sheet stem side up.

4. Pour ½ teaspoon of olive oil over each mushroom and bake 20–30 minutes.

5. Meanwhile, heat the remaining 1 tablespoon of olive oil in a nonstick skillet over medium heat.

6. Add the onion and garlic and sauté for 5 minutes. Add the zucchini and bell pepper and continue to sauté 10–15 minutes until soft. Add the diced tomatoes and chives and cook for 5 minutes more, then season the vegetables with the lemon juice and salt and pepper, to taste.

7. Remove the mushrooms from the oven. Fill each mushroom cap with the vegetable mixture and serve.

NUTRITION · DATA FOR 1 SERVING:

Calories **194kcal**	Sodium **33mg**
Total Carbohydrates **18g**	Potassium **318mg**
Protein **9g**	Dietary Fiber **9g**
Total Fat **11g**	Sugars **7g**
Saturated Fat **2g**	Vitamin A **28% Daily Value**
Polyunsaturated Fat **1g**	Vitamin C **107% Daily Value**
Monounsaturated Fat **8g**	Calcium **2% Daily Value**
Trans Fat **0g**	Iron **2% Daily Value**
Cholesterol **0mg**	

Tortilla Española

Serves: 4

INGREDIENTS

2 tbsp. olive oil

2 small/medium potatoes, scrubbed and diced

1 Italian sausage, sliced (5 oz.)

1 onion, peeled and sliced thin

3 cloves garlic, minced

1 small/medium red bell pepper, seeded and sliced

6 eggs, beaten

salt and pepper, to taste

INSTRUCTIONS

1. Preheat the oven to 375°F.

2. In a large cast iron skillet or Dutch oven, heat the olive oil over medium heat.

3. Add the potatoes, sausage, onion, and garlic and sauté until the potatoes are soft, the onions are translucent and the sausage is cooked through.

4. Add the bell pepper and toss to combine.

5. In a bowl, beat the eggs well and season with salt and pepper.

6. Pour the eggs over the potatoes and sausages in the skillet and swirl around so the eggs coat the pan evenly.

7. Place the cast iron skillet in the oven and bake for approximately 20 minutes or until eggs are cooked through. When the center is set and the top is slightly brown, the tortilla is done.

NUTRITION · DATA FOR 1 SERVING:

Calories **455kcal**	Sodium **1123mg**
Total Carbohydrates **20g**	Potassium **631mg**
Protein **19g**	Dietary Fiber **3g**
Total Fat **33g**	Sugars **3g**
Saturated Fat **10g**	Vitamin A **25% Daily Value**
Polyunsaturated Fat **4g**	Vitamin C **93% Daily Value**
Monounsaturated Fat **16g**	Calcium **3% Daily Value**
Trans Fat **0.2g**	Iron **10% Daily Value**
Cholesterol **52mg**	

8. Remove from the oven and allow to sit for 5 minutes. Run a knife around the outside of the skillet and invert onto a round platter. Serve at room temperature.

Lunch
RECIPES

Avgolemono Lemon Chicken Soup

Serves: 6

INGREDIENTS

1 tbsp. extra-virgin olive oil

½ to 1 cup carrots, finely chopped

½ to 1 cup celery, finely chopped

½ to 1 cup green onions, finely chopped

2 cloves garlic, finely chopped

8 cups low-sodium chicken broth

2 bay leaves

1 cup white rice

salt and black pepper, to taste

6–8 oz. boneless chicken breast, cooked and shredded (store-bought rotisserie chicken will work)

½ cup freshly squeezed lemon juice

2 large eggs

fresh parsley for garnish (optional)

INSTRUCTIONS

1. Over medium heat, heat the olive oil in a medium saucepan. Add the carrots, celery and green onions. Toss together to sauté briefly, then stir in the garlic.

2. Add the chicken broth and bay leaves, then raise the heat to high. When the liquid comes to a boil, immediately add the rice, salt and pepper. Adjust the heat to medium-low and simmer uncovered for 20 minutes or until the rice is tender. Stir in the cooked chicken.

3. To prepare the egg-lemon sauce, whisk together the lemon juice and eggs in a medium bowl. While whisking, add two ladlefuls of the broth from the cooking pot to help temper the eggs. Once fully combined, add the sauce to the chicken soup and stir. Remove from the heat immediately.

4. Garnish with fresh parsley if you like. Serve hot with your favorite bread and enjoy!

NUTRITION · DATA FOR 1 SERVING:

Calories **266kcal**	Sodium **347mg**
Total Carbohydrates **33g**	Potassium **214mg**
Protein **17g**	Dietary Fiber **0.4g**
Total Fat **7g**	Sugars **2g**
Saturated Fat **2g**	Vitamin A **6% Daily Value**
Polyunsaturated Fat **3g**	Vitamin C **11% Daily Value**
Monounsaturated Fat **2.g**	Calcium **28% Daily Value**
Trans Fat **0.1g**	Iron **9% Daily Value**
Cholesterol **135mg**	

Chicken Souvlaki with Tzatziki

Serves: 4

INGREDIENTS

For the souvlaki marinade:
10 cloves garlic, peeled

2 tbsp. dried oregano

1 tsp. dried rosemary

1 tsp. sweet paprika

1 tsp. each kosher salt
and black pepper

¼ cup extra-virgin
olive oil

¼ cup dry white wine

1 lemon, juiced

For the chicken:
2½ lb. organic boneless
skinless chicken breast,
fat removed, cut into
1½-inch pieces

2 bay leaves

Pita fixings:
Smooth Tzatziki
(page 218)

sliced tomato,
cucumber, onions
and kalamata olives

Greek pita bread

**Ideas to serve alongside
(optional):**
Simple Greek Salad
(page 131)

roasted garlic hummus

mezze platter

INSTRUCTIONS

1. In the bowl of a food processor, combine the garlic, oregano, rosemary, paprika, salt, pepper, olive oil, white wine and lemon juice. Pulse until well combined.

2. Place the chicken in a large bowl and add the bay leaves. Top with the marinade. Toss to combine, making sure the chicken is well coated with the marinade. Cover tightly and refrigerate for at least 2 hours or overnight.

3. Soak 10 to 12 wooden skewers in water for 30 to 40 minutes. Meanwhile, prepare the tzatziki sauce and other fixings, and if you're adding Greek salad or other sides, prepare those as well.

4. Thread the marinated chicken pieces onto the prepared skewers. Reserve the marinade.

5. Brush the grates of an outdoor grill or a griddle with a little oil and heat to medium-high. Place the chicken skewers on the grill (or cook in batches on

NUTRITION · DATA FOR 1 SERVING:

Calories **168kcal**	Sodium **705mg**
Total Carbohydrates **2g**	Potassium **261mg**
Protein **22g**	Dietary Fiber **2g**
Total Fat **8g**	Sugars **1g**
Saturated Fat **2g**	Vitamin A **4% Daily Value**
Monounsaturated Fat **3g**	Vitamin C **8% Daily Value**
Polyunsaturated Fat **1g**	Calcium **33% Daily Value**
Trans Fat **1g**	Iron **12% Daily Value**
Cholesterol **69mg**	

the griddle, if necessary). Cook, turning skewers to grill evenly on all sides and brushing lightly with the remaining marinade, until well browned and the internal temperature registers 155°F on an instant-read thermometer, about 5 minutes total.

6. Discard any leftover marinade. Transfer the chicken to a serving platter and let rest for 3 minutes. Meanwhile, briefly grill the pitas and keep warm.

7. Assemble the pitas: First, spread tzatziki sauce on each pita. Remove the chicken pieces from the skewers. Add the chicken to each pita, then add the veggies and the olives.

8. If you want more items to add to your buffet, consider Greek salad, watermelon salad or roasted garlic hummus.

Italian Oven-Roasted Vegetables

Serves: 6

INGREDIENTS

12 oz. baby potatoes, scrubbed (halved or quartered if large)

12 oz. Campari tomatoes (or grape or cherry tomatoes)

2 zucchini or summer squash, cut into 1-inch pieces

8 oz. baby bella mushrooms, cleaned, ends trimmed

10–12 large garlic cloves, peeled

¼ cup extra-virgin olive oil

½ tbsp. dried oregano

1 tsp. dried thyme

salt and pepper

freshly grated Parmesan cheese for serving (optional)

crushed red pepper flakes (optional)

INSTRUCTIONS

1. Preheat your oven to 375°F. Lightly grease a baking sheet with olive oil.

2. Place the potatoes, tomatoes, zucchini, mushrooms and garlic in a large bowl. Drizzle generously with the olive oil. Add the oregano, thyme, salt and pepper. Toss and mix to combine.

3. Spread potatoes on the prepared pan. Roast in the oven for 10 minutes, then add all the remaining vegetables. Return to the oven to roast for another 20 minutes until the veggies are fork-tender.

4. Serve immediately with a sprinkle of freshly grated Parmesan cheese and crushed red pepper flakes, if desired.

NUTRITION · DATA FOR 1 SERVING:

Calories **88kcal**	Sodium **354mg**
Total Carbohydrates **14g**	Potassium **107 mg**
Protein **3g**	Dietary Fiber **0.8g**
Total Fat **3g**	Sugars **0.4g**
Saturated Fat **0.3g**	Vitamin A **6% Daily Value**
Polyunsaturated Fat **0.2g**	Vitamin C **3% Daily Value**
Monounsaturated Fat **2g**	Calcium **36% Daily Value**
Trans Fat **1g**	Iron **14% Daily Value**
Cholesterol **0.0mg**	

Zesty Lemon Rice

Serves: 6

INGREDIENTS

2 cups long-grain rice

3 tbsp. extra-virgin olive oil

1 medium yellow onion, chopped (just over 1 cup)

1 garlic clove, minced

½ cup orzo pasta

2 lemons, juiced

2 cups low-sodium broth (chicken or vegetable broth will work)

pinch of salt

zest of 1 lemon

large handful fresh parsley, chopped

1 tsp. dried dill weed

INSTRUCTIONS

1. Thoroughly wash the rice and soak for at least 15 minutes in plenty of cold water. You should be able to easily break a grain of rice by simply pressing it between your thumb and index finger. Drain well.

2. In a large saucepan that has a lid, heat the olive oil over medium heat until it is shimmering but not smoking. Add the onions and cook for 3 to 4 minutes until translucent. Add the garlic and orzo pasta. Toss for a short time, until the orzo has gained some color, then stir in the rice. Toss to coat.

3. Add the lemon juice and broth. Bring the liquid to a rolling boil, then reduce the heat to low. Cover and let cook for about 20 minutes or until the liquid is fully absorbed and the rice is tender but not sticky.

4. Remove the rice from the heat. For best results, leave it covered and do not disturb the rice for about 10 minutes. Uncover and stir in the lemon zest, parsley, salt and dill weed. If you desire, add a few slices of lemon on top for garnish. Enjoy!

NUTRITION · DATA FOR 1 SERVING:

Calories **145kcal**	Sodium **53mg**
Total Carbohydrates **18g**	Potassium **130mg**
Protein **3g**	Dietary Fiber **0g**
Total Fat **7g**	Sugars **0.5g**
Saturated Fat g	Vitamin A **5% Daily Value**
Polyunsaturated Fat **2g**	Vitamin C **7% Daily Value**
Monounsaturated Fat **4g**	Calcium **24% Daily Value**
Trans Fat **0.3g**	Iron **15% Daily Value**
Cholesterol **0mg**	

Mediterranean Bean Salad

Serves: 8

INGREDIENTS

1 (15-oz.) can kidney beans, drained and rinsed

1 (15-oz.) can cannellini beans, drained and rinsed

1 (15-oz.) can chickpeas, cooked

1 green bell pepper, cored and chopped

1 red bell pepper, cored and chopped

½ English cucumber, diced

1 cup chopped red onions

1½ tbsp. capers

1 cup chopped fresh parsley

10–15 fresh mint leaves, torn or gently chopped

10–15 fresh basil leaves, torn or gently chopped

For the garlic-Dijon vinaigrette:
¼ cup extra-virgin olive oil

2 tbsp. lemon juice

½ tbsp. Dijon mustard

1–2 cloves garlic, minced

1 tsp. sugar

salt and black pepper, to taste

INSTRUCTIONS

1. In a medium bowl, combine the beans, chickpeas, peppers, cucumbers, onions, capers and fresh herbs. Mix, using a wooden spoon, until evenly combined.

2. In a small bowl, combine all the vinaigrette ingredients. Whisk vigorously to combine.

3. Add the vinaigrette and cucumber to the salad bowl. Toss to coat.

4. For the best results, cover and refrigerate for a bit before serving so that the beans soak up the vinaigrette flavors. Give the salad another quick toss before serving!

NUTRITION · DATA FOR 1 SERVING:

Calories **211kcal**	Sodium **476mg**
Total Carbohydrates **28g**	Potassium **340mg**
Protein **10g**	Dietary Fiber **6g**
Total Fat **8g**	Sugars **4g**
Saturated Fat **1g**	Vitamin A **2% Daily Value**
Polyunsaturated Fat **4g**	Vitamin C **5% Daily Value**
Monounsaturated Fat **2g**	Calcium **6% Daily Value**
Trans Fat **1g**	Iron **15% Daily Value**
Cholesterol **0mg**	

Bulgur & Lime Tabouli

Serves: 6

INGREDIENTS

½ cup extra-fine bulgur wheat

4 Roma tomatoes, very finely chopped

1 English cucumber, very finely chopped

2 bunches parsley, part of the stems removed, washed and well dried, very finely chopped

12–15 fresh mint leaves, stems removed, washed and well dried, very finely chopped

4 green onions, white and green parts, very finely chopped

salt

3–4 tbsp. lime juice (or lemon juice, if you prefer)

3–4 tbsp. extra-virgin olive oil

pita bread to serve (optional)

romaine lettuce leaves to serve (optional)

INSTRUCTIONS

1. Wash the bulgur wheat and soak it in water 5–7 minutes. Drain very well, getting rid of all the excess water. Once drained, cook in boiling water 16-18 minutes or until tender. Set aside.

2. Place the tomatoes in a colander to drain excess juice.

3. Combine the chopped vegetables, herbs and green onions in a mixing bowl or dish. Add the bulgur and season with salt. Mix gently. Add the lime juice and olive oil and mix again.

4. For the best results, cover the tabouli and refrigerate for 30 minutes. Transfer to a serving platter. If you like, serve the tabouli with a side of pita and romaine lettuce leaves, which can act as wraps or "boats" for the tabouli.

NUTRITION · DATA FOR 1 SERVING:

Calories **190kcal**	Sodium **79mg**
Total Carbohydrates **25g**	Potassium **105mg**
Protein **3g**	Dietary Fiber **3g**
Total Fat **10g**	Sugars **8g**
Saturated Fat **3g**	Vitamin A **2% Daily Value**
Polyunsaturated Fat **2g**	Vitamin C **6% Daily Value**
Monounsaturated Fat **3g**	Calcium **13% Daily Value**
Trans Fat **2g**	Iron **9% Daily Value**
Cholesterol **13mg**	

Watermelon & Mint Salad

Serves: 6

INGREDIENTS

For the honey vinaigrette:
2 tbsp. honey

2 tbsp. lime juice

1–2 tbsp. extra-virgin olive oil

pinch of salt

For the watermelon salad:
½ watermelon, peeled, cut into cubes

1 English cucumber, cubed (about 2 cups)

15 fresh mint leaves, chopped

15 fresh basil leaves, chopped

½ cup crumbled feta cheese, or more to taste

INSTRUCTIONS

1. Whisk together the honey, lime juice, olive oil and salt in a small bowl. Set aside.

2. In a large bowl, combine the watermelon, cucumbers and fresh herbs.

3. Top the watermelon salad with the honey vinaigrette and gently toss to combine evenly. Top with the feta cheese and serve!

NUTRITION · DATA FOR 1 SERVING:

Calories **192kcal**	Sodium **119mg**
Total Carbohydrates **36g**	Potassium **126mg**
Protein **4g**	Dietary Fiber **2g**
Total Fat **6g**	Sugars **30g**
Saturated Fat **2g**	Vitamin A **4% Daily Value**
Polyunsaturated Fat **1 g**	Vitamin C **8% Daily Value**
Monounsaturated Fat **0.2 g**	Calcium **16% Daily Value**
Trans Fat **2g**	Iron **11% Daily Value**
Cholesterol **3 mg**	

Traditional Olives & Feta Salad

Serves: 5

INGREDIENTS

4 medium juicy tomatoes, preferably organic

⅓ English cucumber, partially peeled in a striped pattern

1 green bell pepper, cored

1 medium red onion

½ cup pitted Greek kalamata olives

pinch salt

¼ cup extra-virgin olive oil

1–2 tbsp. red wine vinegar

½ cup (4 oz.) Greek feta cheese (do not crumble), or more to taste

½ tbsp. dried oregano

INSTRUCTIONS

1. Slice the tomatoes into wedges or large chunks. Cut the cucumber in half lengthwise, then slice into thick half-moons. Thinly slice the bell pepper into rings.

2. Cut the red onion in half and thinly slice into half-moons.

3. Combine the tomatoes, cucumber, pepper and onion in a large salad dish. Add a good handful of the kalamata olives.

4. Season with the salt, then pour the olive oil and vinegar over the salad.

5. Give everything a very gentle toss to mix. Do not overmix—this salad is not meant to be handled too much.

6. Finally, add the the feta cheese blocks and sprinkle the dried oregano on top. Serve with crusty bread if desired.

NUTRITION · DATA FOR 1 SERVING:

Calories **169kcal**	Sodium **137mg**
Total Carbohydrates **8g**	Potassium **102mg**
Protein **6g**	Dietary Fiber **24g**
Total Fat **14g**	Sugars **47g**
Saturated Fat **4g**	Vitamin A **3% Daily Value**
Polyunsaturated Fat **6g**	Vitamin C **8% Daily Value**
Monounsaturated Fat **3g**	Calcium **12% Daily Value**
Trans Fat **0g**	Iron **15% Daily Value**
Cholesterol **25mg**	

Lemon Chicken Soup

Serves: 6

INGREDIENTS

1 tbsp. extra-virgin olive oil

⅓ cup cubed carrots

½ cup chopped yellow onion

2 tsp. minced fresh garlic

⅓ tsp. crushed red pepper

6 cups unsalted chicken stock

½ cup whole-wheat orzo

3 large eggs

¼ cup fresh lemon juice

3 cups shredded rotisserie chicken

3 cups chopped baby spinach

1¼ tsp. kosher salt

½ tsp. black pepper

3 tbsp. chopped fresh dill

INSTRUCTIONS

1. Heat the oil in a Dutch oven over medium-high heat. Add the carrots and onions and cook, stirring often, until both vegetables are softened, 3–4 minutes. Add the garlic and crushed red pepper and cook, stirring constantly, until fragrant, about 1 minute.

2. Add the stock to the Dutch oven, increase the heat to high and bring to a boil. Add the orzo and cook, uncovered, until orzo is al dente, about 6 minutes.

3. Meanwhile, in a medium bowl whisk the eggs and lemon juice together until frothy. Once the orzo is done, carefully remove 1 cup boiling stock from the Dutch oven. Gradually add the hot stock to the egg–lemon juice mixture, whisking constantly to temper the eggs for about 1 minute. Pour the egg mixture back into the Dutch oven and stir to combine.

4. Lower the heat to medium-low and stir in the chicken, spinach, salt and pepper. Cook, stirring constantly, until the spinach wilts, about 1 minute. Divide the soup among 6 bowls; sprinkle each serving evenly with dill.

NUTRITION · DATA FOR 1 SERVING:

Calories **261kcal**	Sodium **641mg**
Total Carbohydrates **16g**	Potassium **435mg**
Protein **24g**	Dietary Fiber **3g**
Total Fat **8g**	Sugars **3g**
Saturated Fat **2g**	Vitamin A **11% Daily Value**
Polyunsaturated Fat **4g**	Vitamin C **7% Daily Value**
Monounsaturated Fat **1g**	Calcium **24% Daily Value**
Trans Fat **0.5g**	Iron **17% Daily Value**
Cholesterol **34mg**	

Roasted Kale & Chickpea Salad

Serves: 4

INGREDIENTS

3 cups boiling water

½ cup bulgur

2 (15-oz.) cans unsalted chickpeas, rinsed and drained

1½ tbsp. canola oil

2 cups finely chopped carrots

4 cups chopped lacinato kale

½ cup sliced shallots

½ cup fresh flat-leaf parsley leaves

½ tsp. kosher salt, divided

½ tsp. black pepper

½ avocado, peeled and pitted

2 tbsp. extra virgin olive oil

1 tbsp. fresh lemon juice

1 tbsp. tahini (sesame seed paste), well stirred

1 clove garlic

¼ tsp. ground turmeric

INSTRUCTIONS

1. Combine the water and bulgur and cook 14–18 minutes or until tender, drain well and set aside to cool.

2. Pat the chickpeas dry with paper towels. Heat the canola oil in a large skillet over high heat. Add the chickpeas and carrots and cook, stirring occasionally, until chickpeas are browned, about 6 minutes. Add the kale, cover, and cook until the kale is slightly wilted and carrots are tender, about 2 minutes. Add the chickpea mixture, shallots, parsley, ¼ teaspoon of the salt, and the pepper to the bulgur; toss to combine.

3. In a food processor, process the avocado, olive oil, lemon juice, tahini, garlic, turmeric and remaining ¼ teaspoon salt until smooth. Divide the bulgur mixture among 4 bowls and drizzle each serving evenly with the avocado mixture.

NUTRITION · DATA FOR 1 SERVING:

Calories **520kcal**	Sodium **495mg**
Total Carbohydrates **68g**	Potassium **364mg**
Protein **18g**	Dietary Fiber **16g**
Total Fat **20g**	Sugars **7g**
Saturated Fat **2g**	Vitamin A **6% Daily Value**
Polyunsaturated Fat **13g**	Vitamin C **13% Daily Value**
Monounsaturated Fat **4g**	Calcium **28% Daily Value**
Trans Fat **1g**	Iron **10% Daily Value**
Cholesterol **62.7mg**	

Carpaccio

Serves: 4

INGREDIENTS

1 lb. beef filet

½ cup lemon juice

¼ cup red wine (or red wine vinegar, for a nonalcoholic option)

2 tbsp. chopped parsley

2 tbsp. capers, drained

1 small clove garlic, minced

1 tbsp. minced shallots

1 tbsp. prepared mustard

½ cup olive oil

salt, to taste

¼ cup arugula leaves

2 tbsp. freshly shaved Parmesan cheese

INSTRUCTIONS

1. Trim all the fat from the beef, then wrap the filet in foil and place in the freezer for 30 minutes to facilitate slicing.

2. While the meat is in the freezer, make the sauce by combining the lemon juice, wine, parsley, capers, garlic, shallots and mustard in a medium bowl. Gradually pour in the olive oil in a steady stream, whisking constantly, then season with salt and refrigerate for at least 20 minutes.

3. Remove the meat from the freezer. With a very sharp, thin knife, slice meat on a diagonal into paper-thin slices.

4. Place the beef slices on a platter or individual plates. Drizzle over a little of the sauce.

5. Sprinkle the arugula leaves and Parmesan cheese over the filet slices.

6. Serve with either fresh or toasted sliced baguette, and with any additional sauce on the side.

NUTRITION · DATA FOR 1 SERVING:

Calories **513kcal**	Sodium **303mg**
Total Carbohydrates **4g**	Potassium **506mg**
Protein **26g**	Dietary Fiber **0.4g**
Total Fat **43g**	Sugars **1g**
Saturated Fat **9g**	Vitamin A **4% Daily Value**
Polyunsaturated Fat **4g**	Vitamin C **28% Daily Value**
Monounsaturated Fat **27g**	Calcium **7% Daily Value**
Trans Fat **0.4g**	Iron **19% Daily Value**
Cholesterol **75mg**	

Simple Greek Salad

Serves: 6

INGREDIENTS

4 cups mixed salad greens (spinach, arugula, kale, watercress, romaine, etc.)

3 medium tomatoes, diced (or 1½ cups halved cherry tomatoes)

1 large cucumber, sliced

1 cup feta cheese, crumbled

4 scallions, sliced

12 ripe black olives, pitted

1 tbsp. balsamic vinegar

⅓ cup Italian Dressing

INSTRUCTIONS

1. Combine the greens, tomatoes, cucumber, feta cheese, scallions, olives, and vinegar in a large serving bowl.

2. Drizzle with the dressing and lightly toss together.

3. Let stand for up to 15 minutes before serving to allow the flavors to combine.

NUTRITION · DATA FOR 1 SERVING:

Calories **128kcal**	Sodium **458mg**
Total Carbohydrates **8g**	Potassium **313mg**
Protein **5g**	Dietary Fiber **2g**
Total Fat **9g**	Sugars **5g**
Saturated Fat **4g**	Vitamin A **120% Daily Value**
Polyunsaturated Fat **2g**	Vitamin C **19% Daily Value**
Monounsaturated Fat **3g**	Calcium **16% Daily Value**
Trans Fat **4g**	Iron **5% Daily Value**
Cholesterol **22mg**	

Italian Dressing

Makes: 1 cup

INGREDIENTS

½ cup olive oil

2 tbsp. freshly squeezed lemon juice

1 tbsp. white wine vinegar

¼ cup capers, drained

1 clove garlic, minced

1 scallion, minced

1 small dried red chili, sliced

½ tsp. pepper

½ tsp. fennel seed, crushed

INSTRUCTIONS

1. Combine all the ingredients in a jar with a tight-fitting lid and shake well.

2. Store with the lid tightly secured in the refrigerator for up to 7 days.

NUTRITION · DATA FOR 1 SERVING:

Calories **164kcal**	Cholesterol **0mg**
Total Carbohydrates **1g**	Sodium **10mg**
Protein **0g**	Potassium **32mg**
Total Fat **18g**	Dietary Fiber **0g**
Saturated Fat **2g**	Sugars **0g**
Polyunsaturated Fat **2g**	Vitamin A **3% Daily Value**
Monounsaturated Fat **13g**	Vitamin C **16% Daily Value**
Trans Fat **0g**	Calcium **1% Daily Value**

Pickled Herring with Beet Dip Crostini

Serves: 6

INGREDIENTS

For the dip:

1 lb. beets, cooked until soft, then peeled, and cut into chunks

4 oz. labneh

2 tbsp. minced shallots

1 tbsp. apple cider vinegar

½ tsp. ground mustard

½ tsp. dried thyme

½ tsp. dried tarragon

To serve:

8 slices French baguette, toasted

1 tbsp. olive oil

12 oz. pickled herring, drained

½ Spanish onion, peeled and thinly sliced

½ gherkins, thinly sliced

2 tbsp. freshly squeezed lemon juice

INSTRUCTIONS

1. Brush the bread slices with a little olive oil on each side.

2. Place the bread either on a hot grill plate or under a hot broiler and grill on both sides until lightly brown. Remove from the heat and set aside.

3. Meanwhile, combine all the dip ingredients in a food processor or blender and process until smooth.

4. Adjust the seasonings, adding more vinegar to taste.

5. Slather each toast slice with the dip and top with 2 to 3 slices of the pickled herring, slices of the Spanish onion and gherkin, and a squeeze of lemon juice over the top.

6. Serve immediately.

7. Refrigerate any remaining dip in a tightly sealed container for up to 7 days.

NUTRITION · DATA FOR 1 SERVING:

Calories **277kcal**	Sodium **669mg**
Total Carbohydrates **27g**	Potassium **247mg**
Protein **10g**	Dietary Fiber **3g**
Total Fat **15g**	Sugars **11g**
Saturated Fat **4g**	Vitamin A **11% Daily Value**
Polyunsaturated Fat **1g**	Vitamin C **10% Daily Value**
Monounsaturated Fat **6g**	Calcium **7% Daily Value**
Trans Fat **0g**	Iron **8% Daily Value**
Cholesterol **18mg**	

Pita Breads with Roasted Lamb & Vegetables

Serves: 12

INGREDIENTS

For the lamb:
3½ lb. lamb shoulder, on the bone

2 tbsp. lemon juice

1 small clove garlic, peeled and crushed

1 tsp. crushed red pepper

1 tsp. ground coriander

1 tsp. ground ginger

½ tsp. freshly ground black pepper

For the filling:
6 oz. pitted black olives, drained

2 medium tomatoes, diced

1 large red bell pepper, seeded and sliced

1 large zucchini, grated

1 red onion, peeled and thinly sliced

1 cup arugula leaves

¼ cup chopped Italian parsley leaves

2 tbsp. lemon juice

1 tbsp. balsamic vinegar

1 tbsp. olive oil

salt and pepper, to taste

To serve:
6 white pita breads

INSTRUCTIONS

1. Prepare the lamb the day before.

2. Combine the lemon juice, garlic, crushed red pepper, coriander, ginger and black pepper. Rub this marinade all over the lamb, place in a roasting pan, cover with plastic wrap and chill in the fridge overnight.

3. The next day, preheat the oven to 400°F. Remove the lamb from the fridge 30 minutes before cooking to bring to room temperature.

4. Roast the lamb in the oven for 1 hour 20 minutes for rare, or up to 30 minutes longer if you prefer it well-done.

5. When the lamb is cooked, remove it from the oven, cover with foil and let rest for about 30 minutes in the pan.

6. Meanwhile, combine all the filling ingredients in a serving bowl and gently toss together.

NUTRITION · DATA FOR 1 SERVING:	
Calories **526kcal**	Sodium **660mg**
Total Carbohydrates **29g**	Potassium **538mg**
Protein **35g**	Dietary Fiber **2g**
Total Fat **30g**	Sugar **2g**
Saturated Fat **12g**	Vitamin A **25% Daily Value**
Polyunsaturated Fat **3g**	Vitamin C **63% Daily Value**
Monounsaturated Fat **13g**	Calcium **9% Daily Value**
Trans Fat **0.5g**	Iron **25% Daily Value**
Cholesterol **122mg**	

7. Using a very sharp knife, cut the lamb down either side of the bone, and trim and discard all the fat and any sinew. Dice the lamb into 1-inch cubes.

8. Spoon some of the lamb and vegetable filling into each pita bread, season with a little more salt and pepper if you wish, and serve.

Grilled Salmon on Herbed Couscous

Serves: 4

INGREDIENTS

For the grilled salmon:
4 (6-oz.) salmon fillets (about 1½ lb.)

2 tbsp. olive oil

1 tsp. salt

1 tsp. black pepper

1 large zucchini, thinly sliced

For the herbed couscous:
1½ cups vegetable stock

1 tsp. olive oil

1 tbsp. chopped fresh thyme leaves

1 tbsp. chopped fresh parsley

¼ tsp. freshly ground black pepper

1 bay leaf

1 cup couscous

½ cup yellow bell pepper, finely diced

½ cup tomatoes, finely diced

INSTRUCTIONS

1. For the couscous, combine the stock, oil, thyme, parsley, pepper and bay leaf in a small saucepan and bring to a boil.

2. Add the couscous and mix well, then remove from the heat. Cover tightly and allow to stand for at least 5 minutes, or until all of the liquid has been absorbed. Mix in the bell pepper and tomatoes and set aside.

3. Meanwhile, preheat the broiler to high.

4. Rub the surface of the fish with 1 tablespoon of the olive oil and sprinkle with the salt and pepper.

5. Broil 3–4 minutes per side or until the fish is cooked through and just flakes with a fork (do not overcook or the fish will become tough).

6. While the fish is cooking, heat the remaining tablespoon of olive oil in a skillet over medium-high heat. Add the zucchini and cook until just tender and slightly golden, 5–8 minutes.

NUTRITION · DATA FOR 1 SERVING:

Calories **441kcal**	Sodium **748mg**
Total Carbohydrates **39g**	Potassium **423mg**
Protein **38g**	Dietary Fiber **4g**
Total Fat **14g**	Sugars **4g**
Saturated Fat **3g**	Vitamin A **48% Daily Value**
Polyunsaturated Fat **1g**	Vitamin C **27% Daily Value**
Monounsaturated Fat **6g**	Calcium **9% Daily Value**
Trans Fat **0.5g**	Iron **16% Daily Value**
Cholesterol **113mg**	

7. To serve, place a rounded ½ cup of couscous on each of 4 plates. Divide the zucchini among the plates and set a piece of the finished grilled fish over top.

8. Serve with a slice or two of fresh lemon or lime, if desired.

Shrimp & Asparagus Salad

Serves: 4

INGREDIENTS

For the salad:
1 tbsp. olive oil

1 medium onion, peeled and diced

2 cloves garlic, minced

1 lb. asparagus, trimmed and cut into 1½-inch pieces

1 lb. shrimp, cooked, shelled and deveined

2 large tomatoes, cut into wedges

For the dressing:
1 cup mayonnaise

¼ cup freshly squeezed lemon juice

¼ cup finely chopped parsley

1 tbsp. prepared horseradish

½ tsp. sea salt

½ tsp. freshly ground black pepper

½ tsp. celery seed

To serve:
4 lemon wedges

INSTRUCTIONS

1. Heat the olive oil in a skillet over medium-high heat. Add the onion and garlic and sauté 3–5 minutes, or until tender.

2. Add the asparagus and shrimp and continue to sauté, tossing frequently, until the asparagus is barely tender and the shrimp is heated through, approximately 2 minutes. Remove from the heat and place in a serving bowl, then add the tomatoes and toss to combine.

3. In another small bowl, mix together the mayonnaise, lemon juice, parsley, horseradish, salt, pepper and celery seed.

4. Stir the dressing into the shrimp and asparagus salad.

5. Divide among serving bowls and serve each with a slice of lemon.

NUTRITION · DATA FOR 1 SERVING:

Calories **467kcal**	Sodium **444mg**
Total Carbohydrates **26g**	Potassium **680mg**
Protein **35g**	Dietary Fiber **3g**
Total Fat **26g**	Sugars **8g**
Saturated Fat **4g**	Vitamin A **35% Daily Value**
Polyunsaturated Fat **12g**	Vitamin C **50% Daily Value**
Monounsaturated Fat **8g**	Calcium **2% Daily Value**
Trans Fat **0.1g**	Iron **40% Daily Value**
Cholesterol **242mg**	

Sicilian Eggplant Caponata

Serves: 8

INGREDIENTS

2 tbsp. olive oil, plus more as needed

1 large eggplant, cut into 1-inch cubes

salt and pepper, to taste

2 medium onions, peeled and diced

3 celery stalks, sliced

1 lb. canned Italian plum tomatoes

10 green olives, pitted and quartered

2 cloves garlic, crushed

¼ cup white wine vinegar

2 tbsp. sugar

½ cup pine nuts

¼ cup capers

INSTRUCTIONS

1. Heat the olive oil in a large nonstick skillet over medium-high heat. Season the eggplant with salt and pepper. Add to the skillet and cook until tender, about 4–6 minutes. Remove from the pan and set aside.

2. Add the onion to the skillet, increasing a little more olive oil if necessary, and sauté until tender. Add the celery, tomatoes, olives and garlic. Reduce the heat to medium-low and cook for 10 minutes more.

3. Meanwhile, heat the vinegar in a small saucepan over medium heat. Stir in the sugar until it is dissolved.

4. Return the cooked eggplant to the skillet and add the pine nuts and capers.

5. Add the vinegar mixture to the skillet and mix thoroughly.

6. Season with salt and pepper, to taste, and cook for 5 minutes longer.

7. Serve chilled on top of a sliced baguette, grilled crostini or fresh slices of your preferred Italian-style bread.

NUTRITION · DATA FOR 1 SERVING:

Calories **158kcal**	Sodium **441mg**
Total Carbohydrates **13g**	Potassium **375mg**
Protein **3g**	Dietary Fiber **4g**
Total Fat **11g**	Sugars **7g**
Saturated Fat **1g**	Vitamin A **8% Daily Value**
Polyunsaturated Fat **3g**	Vitamin C **16% Daily Value**
Monounsaturated Fat **6g**	Calcium **3% Daily Value**
Trans Fat **0g**	Iron **7% Daily Value**
Cholesterol **0mg**	

Spinach Torta

Serves: 6

INGREDIENTS

1 (10-oz.) pie crust, premade or frozen

1 tbsp. Dijon mustard

For the filling:
4 tbsp. butter

9 oz. frozen spinach, thawed and well drained

½ cup red onion, peeled and diced

¼ cup chopped, dry (not oil-packed) sun-dried tomatoes

1 tsp. dried Italian seasoning

½ tsp. dried oregano leaves

¼ tsp. garlic powder

¼ tsp. salt

4 eggs, beaten

2 cups shredded mozzarella cheese

INSTRUCTIONS

1. Preheat the oven to 450°F.

2. Thaw the pie crust according to the package directions. Prepare a 10-inch slightly greased springform pan.

3. Place the crust in the pan, pressing into the bottom and up the sides. Spread the mustard over the bottom of the crust and bake 9–11 minutes or until the crust is lightly browned. Cool on a wire rack.

4. Reduce the oven temperature to 350°F.

5. Melt the butter in a large skillet over medium-low heat.

6. Add the spinach, onion and sun-dried tomatoes. Cook and stir for 5 to 7 minutes or until the onion is crisp-tender. Remove from the heat, then add the Italian seasoning, oregano, garlic powder and salt. Mix well.

NUTRITION · DATA FOR 1 SERVING:

Calories **499kcal**	Sodium **810mg**
Total Carbohydrates **29g**	Potassium **317mg**
Protein **19g**	Dietary Fiber **4g**
Total Fat **35g**	Sugars **3g**
Saturated Fat **14g**	Vitamin A **114% Daily Value**
Polyunsaturated Fat **5g**	Vitamin C **20% Daily Value**
Monounsaturated Fat **12g**	Calcium **38% Daily Value**
Trans Fat **2.2g**	Iron **19% Daily Value**
Cholesterol **181mg**	

7. In a large bowl, combine the eggs and cheese. Mix well. Stir in the spinach mixture until well combined.

8. Spoon evenly into the partially baked crust, and bake for 25 to 35 minutes or until golden brown on top.

9. Allow to stand for 10 minutes before removing from the pan and slicing.

Tuna-Stuffed Eggplants

Serves: 4

INGREDIENTS

2 large eggplants

1–2 tsp. coarsely ground sea salt

¼ cup olive oil

2 tomatoes, diced

1½ cups fresh bread crumbs

7 oz. canned tuna in water, drained

6 anchovy fillets, finely chopped

½ cup finely minced black olives

2 tbsp. minced capers

1 tbsp. finely chopped basil

1 tbsp. chopped Italian parsley

½ cup grated mozzarella cheese

½ cup crumbled feta cheese

INSTRUCTIONS

1. Preheat the oven to 375°F.

2. Cut the eggplants in half lengthwise and scoop out the flesh, leaving a ½-inch shell. Finely dice the pulp, sprinkle well with salt and place in a colander set in the sink.

3. Sprinkle the insides of the eggplant shells with salt and place them cut side down on a paper towel. Allow the eggplant pulp and shells to drain for 30 minutes.

4. Heat the olive oil in a large skillet over high heat. Add the well-drained eggplant pulp and cook until lightly browned. Add the tomatoes and stir until the liquid has evaporated, about 12 minutes.

5. Add the bread crumbs, tuna, anchovies, olives, capers, basil and parsley. Cook the mixture for 2 more minutes.

NUTRITION · DATA FOR 1 SERVING

Calories **602kcal**	Sodium **244mg**
Total Carbohydrates **47g**	Potassium **893mg**
Protein **32g**	Dietary Fiber **13g**
Total Fat **33g**	Sugars **11g**
Saturated Fat **11g**	Vitamin A **23% Daily Value**
Polyunsaturated Fat **2g**	Vitamin C **27% Daily Value**
Monounsaturated Fat **13g**	Calcium **34% Daily Value**
Trans Fat **2.0g**	Iron **26% Daily Value**
Cholesterol **64mg**	

6. Place the eggplant shells in a foil-lined baking dish. Divide the eggplant-tomato mixture among the shells and sprinkle over the grated mozzarella cheese and crumbled feta cheese. Place in the oven and bake for 1 hour. Serve hot and crispy!

Tuscan Tuna Salad

Serves: 4

INGREDIENTS

14 oz. canned tuna in water, drained

8 oz. canned chickpeas, drained and rinsed

3 cups arugula leaves

1 large tomato, seeded and diced

1 small/medium cucumber, halved lengthwise and sliced

½ cup thinly sliced red onion

⅓ cup sliced olives

2 tbsp. capers

2 tbsp. chopped fresh basil leaves

¼ cup Italian dressing

INSTRUCTIONS

1. Combine all the ingredients except the dressing in a bowl. Add the Italian dressing and lightly toss together.

2. Divide among serving bowls and serve immediately.

NUTRITION · DATA FOR 1 SERVING:

Calories **262kcal**	Sodium **983mg**
Total Carbohydrates **21g**	Potassium **605mg**
Protein **29g**	Dietary Fiber **4g**
Total Fat **7g**	Sugars **5g**
Saturated Fat **1g**	Vitamin A **19% Daily Value**
Polyunsaturated Fat **3g**	Vitamin C **22% Daily Value**
Monounsaturated Fat **2g**	Calcium **8% Daily Value**
Trans Fat **0.5g**	Iron **18% Daily Value**
Cholesterol **30mg**	

Tuscan Sausage & Bean Soup

Serves: 4

INGREDIENTS

3 mild Italian sausages, sliced ½ inch thick

14 oz. canned cannellini beans, drained and rinsed

2 celery stalks, sliced

1 large zucchini, sliced

1 large carrot, sliced

1 medium onion, peeled and diced

3 cups beef stock

8 oz. tomato purée

3 tbsp. chopped fresh basil

salt and pepper, to taste

½ cup freshly grated Parmesan cheese

INSTRUCTIONS

1. Heat a large saucepan over medium-high heat. Add the sliced sausages and cook until browned on all sides, about 8-12 minutes, then drain off any excess fat.

2. Add the beans, celery, zucchini, carrot and onion and cook, stirring, for 2 minutes.

3. Add the beef stock, tomato purée and basil and mix thoroughly.

4. Bring to a boil, then reduce the heat to low and allow to simmer, uncovered, for approximately 30 minutes, or until the soup has thickened and the vegetables are tender.

5. Season with salt and pepper, to taste.

6. Ladle into bowls and garnish with grated Parmesan cheese.

NUTRITION · DATA FOR 1 SERVING:

Calories **443kcal**	Sodium **2070mg**
Total Carbohydrates **39g**	Potassium **1303mg**
Protein **25g**	Dietary Fiber **8g**
Total Fat **22g**	Sugars **9g**
Saturated Fat **8g**	Vitamin A **108% Daily Value**
Polyunsaturated Fat **3g**	Vitamin C **49% Daily Value**
Monounsaturated Fat **9g**	Calcium **22% Daily Value**
Trans Fat **1.3g**	Iron **26% Daily Value**
Cholesterol **43mg**	

Dinner

RECIPES

Mediterranean Baked Cod with Lemon & Garlic

Serves: 4

INGREDIENTS

¼ cup, plus 1 tbsp. fresh lemon juice

5 tbsp extra-virgin olive oil

2 tbsp. butter, melted

⅓ cup all-purpose flour

1 tsp. ground coriander

⅓ tsp. sweet Spanish paprika

⅓ tsp. ground cumin

⅓ tsp. salt

½ tsp. black pepper

1½ lb. cod fillets (4–6 pieces)

5 cloves garlic, minced

¼ cup chopped fresh parsley leaves

INSTRUCTIONS

1. Preheat the oven to 400°F. In a shallow bowl, combine the lemon juice, 3 tablespoons of olive oil, and melted butter. Set aside.

2. In another shallow bowl, combine the all-purpose flour, coriander, paprika, cumin, salt and pepper.

3. Pat the fish fillets dry. Dip each fillet in the lemon juice mixture, then dip in the flour mixture. Shake off excess flour and set the fillets aside in a single layer (not touching one another). Reserve the remaining lemon juice mixture.

4. Heat the remaining 2 tablespoons of olive oil in a cast iron skillet over medium-high heat. When the oil is shimmering, but not smoking, add the fish and sear on each side just enough to give it some color, about 4 minutes per side. It will not be fully cooked. Remove from the heat.

recipe continues

NUTRITION · DATA FOR 1 SERVING:

Calories **312kcal**	Sodium **287mg**
Total Carbohydrates **16g**	Potassium **706mg**
Protein **23g**	Dietary Fiber **7g**
Total Fat **18g**	Sugars **2g**
Saturated Fat **2g**	Vitamin A **4% Daily Value**
Polyunsaturated Fat **10g**	Vitamin C **1% Daily Value**
Monounsaturated Fat **5g**	Calcium **18% Daily Value**
Trans Fat **0g**	Iron **4% Daily Value**
Cholesterol **40mg**	

5. Add the minced garlic to the reserved lemon juice mixture and mix. Drizzle all over the fish fillets.

6. Transfer the skillet to the oven and bake for 10 minutes, until the fish begins to flake easily with a fork. Remove from the oven and sprinkle chopped parsley over the top.

7. You can serve immediately with the Mediterranean Chickpea Salad (page 223).

Chicken Shawarma

Serves: 6

INGREDIENTS

For the chicken:
⅓ tbsp. ground cumin

⅓ tbsp. ground turmeric

⅓ tbsp. ground coriander

⅓ tbsp. garlic powder

⅓ tbsp. paprika

½ tsp. ground cloves

½ tsp. cayenne pepper, or more to taste

8 boneless, skinless chicken thighs

1 tsp. salt

1 large onion, thinly sliced

1 large lemon, juiced

⅓ cup extra-virgin olive oil

To serve:
6 pita pockets

Tahini Sauce (page 219) or Smooth Tzatziki (page 218)

baby arugula

pickles or kalamata olives (optional)

INSTRUCTIONS

1. In a small bowl, combine the cumin, turmeric, coriander, garlic powder, paprika, cloves and cayenne pepper. Set aside the shawarma spice mix.

2. Pat the chicken thighs dry and season them with salt on both sides, then thinly slice into small bite-sized pieces.

3. Transfer the sliced chicken to a large bowl. Add the shawarma spices and toss to coat. Add the onions, lemon juice and olive oil. Toss everything together again.

4. Cover tightly and refrigerate for 3 hours or overnight. If you're really busy, you can skip this step or reduce the time by half.

5. Once everything is ready, preheat your oven to 425°F. Remove the chicken from the fridge and let it sit at room temperature for a few minutes.

recipe continues

NUTRITION · DATA FOR 1 SERVING:

Calories **227kcal**	Sodium **403mg**
Total Carbohydrates **22g**	Potassium **350mg**
Protein **17g**	Dietary Fiber **3g**
Total Fat **15g**	Sugars **4g**
Saturated Fat **2g**	Vitamin A **1% Daily Value**
Polyunsaturated Fat **6g**	Vitamin C **3% Daily Value**
Monounsaturated Fat **5g**	Calcium **22% Daily Value**
Trans Fat **0g**	Iron **8% Daily Value**
Cholesterol **64.6mg**	

6. Spread the marinated chicken with the onions in a single layer on a large, lightly oiled baking sheet. Roast for 30 minutes.

7. To get a more browned, crispier chicken, move the pan to the top rack and broil very briefly, 2–3 minutes. Remove the chicken from the oven.

8. To serve, open the pita pockets up. Add a little Smooth Tzatziki sauce and/or Tahini Sauce to each pocket, then add the chicken shawarma, arugula, and pickles or olives. Serve immediately!

Moroccan Vegetable Tagine

Serves: 6

INGREDIENTS

¼ cup extra-virgin olive oil, plus more for serving

2 medium yellow onions, peeled and chopped

2 large carrots, peeled and chopped

2 large russet potatoes, peeled and cubed

1 large sweet potato, peeled and cubed

8–10 cloves garlic, peeled and chopped

1 tsp. salt

1 tbsp. harissa spice blend

1 tsp. ground coriander

1 tsp. ground cinnamon

½ tsp. ground turmeric

2 cups canned tomatoes, chopped

heaping ½ cup chopped dried apricots

1 quart low-sodium vegetable broth (or broth of your choice)

2 cups cooked chickpeas

1 lemon, juiced

handful of fresh parsley leaves

INSTRUCTIONS

1. In a medium pot or Dutch oven, heat the olive oil over medium heat until it is just shimmering. Add the onions and increase the heat to medium-high. Sauté for 5 minutes, tossing regularly.

2. Add the carrots, russet potatoes, sweet potato, and garlic. Season with the salt and spices and toss to combine evenly. Cook for 5 to 7 minutes, mixing regularly with a wooden spoon.

3. Add the tomatoes, apricots and broth. Season again with just a small dash more salt.

4. Cook for 10 minutes, keeping the heat on medium-high. Then reduce the heat to low, cover and simmer for another 20 to 25 minutes, or until the veggies are tender.

5. Stir in the chickpeas and cook another 5 minutes. Stir in the lemon juice and fresh parsley. Taste and adjust the seasoning, adding more salt or harissa spice blend according to your preference.

recipe continues

NUTRITION · DATA FOR 1 SERVING:

Calories **448kcal**	Sodium **405mg**
Total Carbohydrates **60g**	Potassium **785mg**
Protein **16g**	Dietary Fiber **8g**
Total Fat **18g**	Sugars **22.5g**
Saturated Fat **2g**	Vitamin A **4% Daily Value**
Polyunsaturated Fat **8g**	Vitamin C **8% Daily Value**
Monounsaturated Fat **4g**	Calcium **28% Daily Value**
Trans Fat **4g**	Iron **10% Daily Value**
Cholesterol **2mg**	

6. Transfer the tagine to serving bowls and top each serving with a generous drizzle of extra-virgin olive oil. Serve hot with your favorite bread, couscous or rice. Enjoy!

Seafood Paella

Serves: 6

INGREDIENTS

3 cups water

4 small lobster tails (6–12 oz. each)

3 tbsp. extra-virgin olive oil

1 large yellow onion, chopped

2 cups Spanish rice or medium-grain rice, soaked in water for 20 minutes, then drained

4 cloves garlic, chopped

2 large pinches Spanish saffron threads, soaked in ½ cup water

1 tsp. sweet Spanish paprika

1 tsp. cayenne pepper

½ tsp. Aleppo pepper (or other chili pepper flakes)

1 tsp. salt

2 large Roma tomatoes, finely chopped

6 oz. French green beans, trimmed

1 lb. prawns or large shrimp of your choice, peeled and deveined

¼ cup chopped fresh parsley

INSTRUCTIONS

1. In a large saucepan, bring the 3 cups of water to a boil. Add the lobster tails and boil gently 1–2 minutes, until pink. Turn the heat off. With a pair of tongs, remove the lobster tails and set aside to cool. Do not discard the lobster cooking water. When the lobster is cool enough to handle, remove and discard the shells and cut the lobster into large chunks.

2. In a large, deep pan or cast-iron skillet, heat the olive oil over medium-high heat. Add the onions and sauté for 2 minutes, then add the rice. Cook for 3 more minutes, stirring regularly. Add the chopped garlic and the lobster cooking water. Stir in the saffron and its soaking liquid, and the paprika, cayenne pepper, Aleppo pepper and salt.

3. Stir in the tomatoes and green beans. Bring to a boil for 10 minutes to let the liquid slightly reduce, then turn down the heat to low, cover and cook for 20 minutes.

recipe continues

NUTRITION · DATA FOR 1 SERVING:

Calories **516kcal**	Sodium **507mg**
Total Carbohydrates **61g**	Potassium **403mg**
Protein **41g**	Dietary Fiber **3g**
Total Fat **21g**	Sugars **0g**
Saturated Fat **10g**	Vitamin A **10% Daily Value**
Polyunsaturated Fat **4g**	Vitamin C **4% Daily Value**
Monounsaturated Fat **5g**	Calcium **41% Daily Value**
Trans Fat **2g**	Iron **17% Daily Value**
Cholesterol **12mg**	

4. Uncover and spread the shrimp over the rice, slightly pushing it into the rice. Add a little water if you need to. Cover and cook for another 10 minutes or until the shrimp turns pink. Finally, add the cooked lobster chunks. When the lobster is warmed through, turn off the heat. Garnish with parsley.

5. Serve the paella hot and enjoy!

Traditional Greek Roasted Vegetables (Briam)

Serves: 6

INGREDIENTS

1¼ lb. Yukon Gold potatoes (about 3 medium-size potatoes), peeled and thinly sliced into rounds about ⅛ inch thick

1¼ lb. zucchini squash (2 to 3 zucchini), thinly sliced into rounds about ¼ inch thick

1 tsp. kosher salt

1 tsp. black pepper

2 tsp. dried oregano

1 scant tsp. dried rosemary

½ cup chopped fresh parsley

4 cloves garlic, minced

2 tbsp. extra-virgin olive oil, plus more for serving

1 (28-oz.) can diced tomatoes with juice (preferably no-salt-added organic tomatoes)

1 large red onion or 2 smaller red onions, thinly sliced into rounds (if large, you'll want to cut the onion in half first, then slice)

INSTRUCTIONS

1. Preheat the oven to 400°F. Arrange a rack in the middle.

2. Place the sliced potatoes and zucchini in a large mixing bowl. Season with the salt, pepper, oregano and rosemary. Add the fresh parsley, garlic and a generous drizzle of extra-virgin olive oil. Toss and mix to make sure the vegetables are well coated with the oil and spices.

3. On a baking pan or in a very large, oven-safe skillet, spread half of the canned diced tomatoes to cover the bottom of the pan.

4. Arrange the seasoned potatoes and zucchini and the sliced onions in the pan, working in rows and alternating the veggies in a pattern.

5. If you have any oil-garlic mixture left in the mixing bowl, pour that all over the veggies, then top with the remaining diced tomatoes.

recipe continues

NUTRITION · DATA FOR 1 SERVING:

Calories **68kcal**	Sodium **13mg**
Total Carbohydrates **10g**	Potassium **18mg**
Protein **2g**	Dietary Fiber **6g**
Total Fat **6g**	Sugars **3g**
Saturated Fat **2g**	Vitamin A **6% Daily Value**
Polyunsaturated Fat **3g**	Vitamin C **8% Daily Value**
Monounsaturated Fat **2g**	Calcium **47% Daily Value**
Trans Fat **0g**	Iron **16% Daily Value**
Cholesterol **0mg**	

6. Cover the pan with foil, making sure it's not touching the veggies. Bake for 45 minutes. Take the pan out briefly to carefully remove the foil, then place back in the oven, uncovered, and roast for another 30 to 40 minutes, or until the veggies are soft and charred and most of the liquid has evaporated.

7. Remove from the oven. Add a generous drizzle of extra-virgin olive oil and serve warm or at room temperature.

Kofta Kebab

Makes: 10 skewers

INGREDIENTS

1 medium yellow onion, quartered

2 cloves garlic

1 bunch parsley, stems removed (about 2 packed cups parsley leaves), plus more for serving

1 lb. ground beef

½ lb. ground lamb

1 slice bread, toasted until browned and soaked in water until fully toft

1 tsp. salt

1 tsp. black pepper

1½ tsp. ground allspice

½ tsp. cayenne pepper

½ tsp. ground green cardamom

½ tsp. ground sumac

½ tsp. ground nutmeg

½ tsp. paprika

For serving:
pita bread

Tahini Sauce (page 219)

tomato wedges

onion wedges

INSTRUCTIONS

1. Begin by soaking 10 wooden skewers in water for 30 minutes to 1 hour. Remove from the water when you are ready to begin. Lightly grease the grates of a gas grill and preheat to medium-high for about 20 minutes. Prepare the pita bread and fixings and any other sides before you begin grilling.

2. In a food processor, chop the onion, garlic and parsley.

3. Add the beef and lamb. Squeeze all the water out of the bread and add to the food processor, then add all the spices. Run the processor until the ingredients are well combined and form a pasty mixture.

4. Transfer the meat mixture to a large bowl. Take a fistful of the mixture and mold it onto a wooden skewer to create a kebab about 1 inch thick. Set the skewered kebab on a parchment paper–lined tray. Repeat the process until you have no meat left.

recipe continues

NUTRITION · DATA FOR 1 SERVING:

Calories **197kcal**	Sodium **1178mg**
Total Carbohydrates **3g**	Potassium **314mg**
Protein **18g**	Dietary Fiber **1g**
Total Fat **12g**	Sugars **0g**
Saturated Fat **5g**	Vitamin A **3% Daily Value**
Polyunsaturated Fat **2g**	Vitamin C **9% Daily Value**
Monounsaturated Fat **4g**	Calcium **31% Daily Value**
Trans Fat **1g**	Iron **10% Daily Value**
Cholesterol **63mg**	

5. Place the kebabs on the grill. Grill for 4 minutes on one side, then turn over and grill for another 3 to 4 minutes.

6. Serve your kofta kebabs immediately with pita bread, tahini, and tomato and onion wedges.

Rosemary Baked Chicken

Serves: 6

INGREDIENTS

2 lb. boneless, skinless chicken breasts

1 tsp. salt

1 tsp. black pepper

2 tsp. dried oregano

1 tsp. fresh thyme leaves (from about 2 sprigs thyme)

1 tsp. sweet paprika

4 cloves garlic, minced

3 tbsp. extra-virgin olive oil, plus more for the pan

½ lemon, juiced

1 medium red onion, halved and thinly sliced

5 to 6 Campari tomatoes (or small Roma tomatoes), halved

handful fresh parsley, chopped for garnish

fresh basil leaves, for garnish

fresh rosemary leaves, chopped for garnish

INSTRUCTIONS

1. Preheat the oven to 375°F.

2. Pat the chicken dry. Place the chicken breasts in a large zip-top bag, remove any air from the bag and seal the top, and set the bag on a cutting board. Pound the chicken with a meat mallet to flatten to about ¼ inch thick. Remove the chicken from the zip-top bag and set aside. Reuse the bag and mallet to repeat the process with the remaining chicken breast pieces.

3. Season the chicken with salt and pepper on both sides and place in a large bowl or dish. Add the spices, garlic, olive oil and lemon juice. Combine to make sure the chicken is evenly coated.

4. Grease a baking dish or pan with olive oil, then spread the onion slices on the bottom. Arrange the seasoned chicken over the onions, and top with the tomatoes.

5. Cover the baking dish tightly with foil and bake for 10 minutes, then uncover and bake another 8–10 minutes. Watch carefully because

recipe continues

NUTRITION · DATA FOR 1 SERVING:

Calories **290kcal**	Sodium **272.5mg**
Total Carbohydrates **11g**	Potassium **124.6mg**
Protein **35.9g**	Dietary Fiber **2g**
Total Fat **11.5g**	Sugars **5g**
Saturated Fat **2g**	Vitamin A **7% Daily Value**
Polyunsaturated Fat **1g**	Vitamin C **15% Daily Value**
Monounsaturated Fat **6g**	Calcium **18% Daily Value**
Trans Fat **2.5g**	Iron **21% Daily Value**
Cholesterol **51 mg**	

the cooking time will vary depending on the thickness of your chicken pieces. To make sure the chicken is cooked through, use a digital instant-read or meat thermometer to check for the proper internal temperature of 165°F.

6. Remove the chicken from the oven, cover with foil or another pan and let rest 5–10 minutes. Uncover and garnish with fresh parsley, basil and rosemary. Serve and enjoy!

Moroccan Lamb Stew

Serves: 7

INGREDIENTS

2 tbsp. extra-virgin olive oil, plus more as needed

1 large yellow onion, chopped

3 carrots, chopped

6 Yukon Gold potatoes (or any small potatoes), peeled and ½-inch cubed

3 large cloves garlic, roughly chopped

1½ tsp. kosher salt

1½ tsp. black pepper

2.5 lb. boneless leg of lamb, fat trimmed, cut into cubes (or boneless lamb shoulder, fat trimmed)

½ cup dried apricots

1 cinnamon stick

1 bay leaf

1½ tsp. ground allspice

1½ tsp. Moroccan spice, such as ras el hanout

½ tsp. ground ginger

6 canned, peeled plum tomatoes, halved

2½ cups low-sodium beef broth

1 (15-oz.) can chickpeas

INSTRUCTIONS

1. Preheat the oven to 350°F.

2. In a medium Dutch oven, heat the olive oil over medium heat until shimmering.

3. Add the onions, carrots and potatoes and sauté for 4 minutes. Add the garlic and cook for an additional 3 minutes and season with salt and pepper. Transfer the vegetables to a plate and set aside.

4. Add the lamb to the same pot, adding more oil if needed, and cook until deeply brown on all sides, about

5. 8–12 minutes. Season with salt and pepper.

6. Adjust the heat to medium-high and return the sautéed vegetables to the pot. Add the dried apricots, cinnamon stick, bay leaf, allspice, moroccan spice and ginger and stir to coat.

7. Add the plum tomatoes and broth and bring everything to a boil for 5 minutes.

recipe continues

NUTRITION · DATA FOR 1 SERVING:

Calories **431kcal**	Sodium **167 mg**
Total Carbohydrates **56g**	Potassium **96mg**
Protein **37g**	Dietary Fiber **3g**
Total Fat **8g**	Sugars **8g**
Saturated Fat **2g**	Vitamin A **4% Daily Value**
Polyunsaturated Fat **4g**	Vitamin C **18% Daily Value**
Monounsaturated Fat **1g**	Calcium **31% Daily Value**
Trans Fat **2g**	Iron **29% Daily Value**
Cholesterol **48mg**	

8. Cover the pot and place in the oven for 1½ hours (check partway through to see if more water or broth is needed). Stir in the chickpeas, cover and return to the oven for another 30 minutes.

9. Remove from the oven and serve hot with your choice of rice, couscous, pita bread or your favorite rustic bread.

Authentic Falafel

Serves: 24 portions

INGREDIENTS

2 cups dried chickpeas
(do not use canned or
cooked chickpeas)

½ tsp. baking soda

1 cup fresh parsley

⅓ cup fresh cilantro
leaves

½ cup fresh dill fronds

1 small onion, quartered

7–8 cloves garlic, peeled

salt, to taste

1 tbsp. ground black
pepper

1 tbsp. ground cumin

1 tbsp. ground coriander

1 tsp. cayenne pepper
(optional)

1 tsp. baking powder

2 tbsp. toasted sesame
seeds

canola oil for frying

Homemade Tahini Paste
(page 220)

**To serve as sandwiches
(optional):**
12 pita pockets

hummus

English cucumbers,
chopped or diced

tomatoes, chopped or
diced

baby arugula

pickles

INSTRUCTIONS

A day ahead:

1. Combine the dried chickpeas and baking soda
in a large bowl and fill with water to cover the
chickpeas by at least 2 inches.

2. Soak for at least 18 hours or longer if the
chickpeas are still very hard.

When ready to make the falafel:

3. Drain the chickpeas completely and pat them
dry. Transfer to the large bowl of a food processor
fitted with the chopping blade.

4. Add the herbs, onions, garlic, salt, pepper,
cumin, coriander, and cayenne pepper, if using, to
the chickpeas. Run the food processor 40 seconds
at a time until the falafel mixture is well combined.

5. Transfer the falafel mixture to a container and
cover tightly. Refrigerate for at least 1 hour or a
maximum of 24 hours.

When ready to cook:

6. Add the baking powder and sesame seeds to
the falafel mixture and stir with a spoon.

recipe continues

NUTRITION · DATA FOR 1 SERVING:

Calories **93kcal**	Sodium **13mg**
Total Carbohydrates **1g**	Potassium **99mg**
Protein **4g**	Dietary Fiber **4g**
Total Fat **4g**	Sugars **2g**
Saturated Fat **0.4g**	Vitamin A **6% Daily Value**
Polyunsaturated Fat **1g**	Vitamin C **14% Daily Value**
Monounsaturated Fat **2g**	Calcium **21% Daily Value**
Trans Fat **1g**	Iron **17% Daily Value**
Cholesterol **34mg**	

7. Scoop tablespoonfuls of the falafel mixture and form into ½-inch-thick patties. It helps to have wet hands as you form the patties.

8. Fill up a medium saucepan 3 inches with oil. Heat the oil over medium-high until it bubbles softly. Working in batches if necessary, you should carefully drop the falafel patties in the oil and let them fry for 3 to 5 minutes, until crispy and medium brown on the outside. Do not crowd the falafel in the saucepan.

9. Place the fried falafel patties in a colander or on a plate lined with paper towels to drain. Repeat with the remaining patties.

10. Serve the falafel hot next to other small plates with the sauce drizzles over. Or serve the patties in the falafel pita pockets with tahini or hummus, cucumbers, tomatoes, arugula and pickles if desired. Enjoy!

Shakshuka with Tomato Sauce & Pepper

Serves: 6

INGREDIENTS

3 tbsp. extra-virgin olive oil

1 large yellow onion, chopped

2 green bell peppers, chopped

2 cloves garlic, peeled and chopped

1 tsp. ground coriander

1 tsp. sweet paprika

½ tsp. ground cumin

salt and pepper, to taste

6 vine-ripe tomatoes, chopped (about 6 cups chopped tomatoes)

½ cup tomato sauce

6 large eggs

¼ cup chopped fresh parsley

¼ cup chopped fresh mint

pinch of red pepper flakes (optional)

INSTRUCTIONS

1. In a large skillet, heat the olive oil over medium heat. Add the onions, peppers, garlic, spices and a pinch each of salt and pepper. Cook, stirring occasionally, until the vegetables have softened, about 5 minutes.

2. Add the tomatoes and tomato sauce. Cover and let simmer for about 15 minutes. Uncover and cook a bit longer to allow the mixture to reduce and thicken, then taste and adjust the seasoning to your liking.

3. Use a wooden spoon to create 6 wells in the tomato mixture, making sure the indentations are well spaced. Gently crack an egg into each well.

4. Lower the heat, cover the skillet, and cook on low until the egg whites are set, about 3-5 minutes.

5. Uncover and add the fresh parsley and mint. You can add more black pepper or crushed red pepper, if you like. Serve with warm pita, challah bread or your choice of crusty bread.

NUTRITION · DATA FOR 1 SERVING:

Calories **154kcal**	Sodium **86mg**
Total Carbohydrates **14g**	Potassium **100mg**
Protein **9g**	Dietary Fiber **34g**
Total Fat **8g**	Sugars **1g**
Saturated Fat **4g**	Vitamin A **3% Daily Value**
Polyunsaturated Fat **2g**	Vitamin C **18% Daily Value**
Monounsaturated Fat **1g**	Calcium **45% Daily Value**
Trans Fat **1g**	Iron **12% Daily Value**
Cholesterol **192mg**	

Chicken Gyro

Serves: 5

INGREDIENTS

For the chicken:
1.5 lb. chicken breast

1 cup plain Greek yogurt (you can use reduced-fat or fat-free Greek yogurt if you like)

3 tbsp. extra-virgin olive oil, divided

1 large lemon, juiced

2 tbsp. red wine vinegar

3 garlic cloves, minced

1 tbsp. dried oregano

1 tsp. sweet paprika

1 tsp. ground cumin

1 tsp. ground coriander

generous pinch kosher salt

generous pinch ground black pepper

pinch cayenne pepper (optional)

To serve:
5 pita bread

Smooth Tzatziki (page 218)

1 large tomato, sliced

1 cucumber, sliced

1 green pepper, cored and sliced

1 small red onion, sliced into half-moons

1 cup pitted Kalamata olives

INSTRUCTIONS

1. First, marinate the chicken. In a big mixing bowl, combine the yogurt, 1 tbsp. of the olive oil, the red wine vinegar, garlic, oregano, paprika, cumin, coriander, salt, black pepper and cayenne pepper, if using, and mix well. Add the chicken and mix to make sure each piece is well coated with the marinade. Cover and refrigerate for at least 30 minutes, or overnight.

2. When ready to cook, heat the remaining tablespoon olive oil in a nonstick skillet over medium-high heat until shimmering but not smoking. Remove the chicken from the marinade and shake off any excess, then add the chicken to the pan. Cook undisturbed on one side for 5 minutes, until browned. Use tongs to turn the chicken over and cook on the other side for another 5 minutes or until chicken is done.

3. To assemble the chicken gyros, warm up the pita bread in the oven. Spread the tzatziki sauce on top, then add chicken and top with tomato, cucumber, green pepper, red onion and olives as you like. Squeeze the lemon over, wrap the pita up and enjoy!

NUTRITION · DATA FOR 1 SERVING:

Calories **303kcal**	Sodium **159.8mg**
Total Carbohydrates **16.4g**	Potassium **104.6mg**
Protein **36.7g**	Dietary Fiber **2.8g**
Total Fat **10g**	Sugars **4.8g**
Polyunsaturated Fat **5g**	Vitamin A **6% Daily Value**
Monounsaturated Fat **2.6g**	Vitamin C **12% Daily Value**
Saturated Fat **1.7g**	Calcium **35% Daily Value**
Trans Fat **1.3g**	Iron **14% Daily Value**
Cholesterol **55.1mg**	

Sweet Baked Meatballs (Soutzoukakia)

Makes: 16 pieces

INGREDIENTS

For the meatballs:

2 slices whole-wheat or gluten-free bread, toasted to a medium-brown

¼ –⅓ cup milk or water

1.5 lb. lean ground beef

1 small yellow onion, chopped

3 cloves garlic, minced

2 medium eggs

1 tsp. ground cumin

½ tsp. ground cinnamon

½ tsp. dried oregano

½ cup chopped fresh parsley, plus more for garnish

1 tbsp. salt

1 tbsp. black pepper

drizzle of extra-virgin olive oil, plus more for the baking dish

For the red sauce:

2 tbsp. extra-virgin olive oil

1 medium yellow onion, finely chopped

2 cloves garlic, minced

½ cup dry red wine

2 (15-oz.) cans tomato sauce

1 bay leaf

INSTRUCTIONS

1. Place the toasted bread in a small bowl, cover with the milk or water and set aside to soak. When bread is soft and well soaked, squeeze the liquid out completely and discard any remaining milk.

2. Transfer the bread to a large mixing bowl. Add the ground beef, onion, garlic, eggs, cumin, cinnamon, oregano, parsley, salt and pepper. Knead until the meat mixture is well combined. Cover the mixture and let rest in the fridge while you continue on to the next step

3. Preheat the oven to 400°F.

4. In a saucepan or large skillet, heat the olive oil over medium heat until shimmering but not smoking. Add the onions and cook for about 3 minutes, stirring often. Add the garlic and cook for another minute, stirring regularly. Add the red wine and cook to reduce by about half, approximately 10–12 minutes. Then add the

recipe continues

NUTRITION · DATA FOR 1 SERVING:	
Calories **64kcal**	Sodium **178mg**
Total Carbohydrates **7g**	Potassium **96mg**
Protein **2g**	Dietary Fiber **0g**
Total Fat **3g**	Sugars **3g**
Saturated Fat **5g**	Vitamin A **2% Daily Value**
Polyunsaturated Fat **2g**	Vitamin C **5% Daily Value**
Monounsaturated Fat **1g**	Calcium **25% Daily Value**
Trans Fat **2g**	Iron **16% Daily Value**
Cholesterol **29mg**	

⅓ tsp. ground cumin

½ tsp. ground cinnamon

½ tsp. sugar

salt and black pepper, to taste

tomato sauce, bay leaf, cumin, cinnamon, sugar, and salt and pepper, to taste. Bring to a boil, then lower the heat and simmer for 15 minutes.

5. Meanwhile, lightly grease the bottom of a large baking dish with extra-virgin olive oil.

6. Take the meat mixture out of the fridge. Wet your hands and scoop out about 2½ tablespoons of the mixture, then form it into a large, football-shaped meatball. Repeat with the remaining meat mixture to create 15 to 16 elongated meatballs.

7. Arrange the meatballs in the prepared baking dish. Remove the bay leaf from the sauce and top the meatballs with the sauce.

8. Place the baking dish on the middle rack of the oven. Bake for 40 to 45 minutes or until the meatballs are well cooked all the way through (check halfway through to make sure the baking dish is not dry; if needed, add a little bit of water to the bottom of the dish).

9. Remove from the oven and add another drizzle of olive oil. Garnish with parsley and serve over rice or orzo if desired.

Shrimp & Leek Spaghetti

Serves: 4

INGREDIENTS

8 oz. whole-grain spaghetti

1 lb. medium raw shrimp, peeled and deveined

½ tsp. black pepper

½ tsp. kosher salt, divided

1½ tbsp. olive oil, divided

2 cups chopped leeks (1 large leek)

3 cloves garlic

2 cups (about 9 oz.) frozen baby sweet peas

¼ cup heavy cream

2 tsp. lemon zest

2 tbsp. fresh lemon juice

2 tbsp. chopped fresh dill

INSTRUCTIONS

1. Cook the pasta according to the directions on the package, but do not salt the cooking water. Reserving ½ cup of the cooking liquid, drain the pasta, then cover to keep it warm and set aside.

2. While the pasta cooks, pat the shrimp dry with paper towels; season with the pepper and ¼ teaspoon of the salt. Heat half of the olive oil in a large nonstick skillet over high heat. Add the shrimp and cook, stirring often, until cooked through, 3 to 4 minutes. Transfer to a plate and cover to keep warm. (Do not wipe the skillet clean.)

3. Reduce the heat to medium-high. Add the leek, garlic, the remaining oil and the remaining ¼ teaspoon salt. Cook, stirring often, until the leek is slightly tender, 2 to 3 minutes. Add the peas, cream, lemon zest, lemon juice and the reserved ½ cup of the cooking liquid. Reduce the heat to medium and simmer until the sauce thickens slightly, 2 to 3 minutes. Return the shrimp to the skillet and toss to coat.

4. Divide the pasta among 4 bowls and top evenly with the shrimp and sauce. Sprinkle with dill and serve immediately.

NUTRITION · DATA FOR 1 SERVING:

Calories **446kcal**	Sodium **649mg**
Total Carbohydrates **59g**	Potassium **454mg**
Protein **28g**	Dietary Fiber **9g**
Total Fat **13g**	Sugars **8g**
Saturated Fat **5g**	Vitamin A **7% Daily Value**
Polyunsaturated Fat **3g**	Vitamin C **4% Daily Value**
Monounsaturated Fat **4g**	Calcium **14% Daily Value**
Trans Fat **1g**	Iron **16% Daily Value**
Cholesterol **25mg**	

Panko Salmon with Snap Peas

Serves: 4

INGREDIENTS

1½ tbsp. Dijon mustard

1½ tbsp. mayonnaise

½ tsp. kosher salt, divided

½ tsp. black pepper, divided

4 (6-oz.) skinless salmon fillets

½ cup whole-wheat panko (Japanese bread crumbs)

1 tbsp. chopped fresh tarragon, divided

2 tsp. grated lemon rind, divided

2 tbsp. olive oil, divided

2½ cups sugar snap peas

⅓ cup thinly sliced shallots (about 2 medium)

2 tsp. fresh lemon juice

INSTRUCTIONS

1. In a shallow bowl, combine the mustard, mayonnaise, ¼ teaspoon of the salt and ¼ teaspoon of the pepper. Spoon the mustard mixture evenly over the salmon fillets. In a separate small bowl, combine the panko, 1½ teaspoons of the tarragon and 1 teaspoon of the lemon rind. Sprinkle the panko mixture over the mustard-coated side of the fillet, pressing to adhere.

2. Heat 1 tablespoon of the oil in a large nonstick skillet over medium heat. Carefully add the fillets, panko side down, to the pan. Cook 3 to 4 minutes or until golden, then turn and cook on the other side, 3 to 4 minutes, or to your desired degree of doneness. Remove the fillets from the pan; keep warm in foil.

3. Increase the heat to medium-high and add the remaining 1 tablespoon oil to the pan. Add the snap peas and shallots and cook, stirring occasionally, for 3 minutes. Add the remaining ¼ teaspoon salt, ¼ teaspoon pepper, 1½ teaspoons

---

NUTRITION · DATA FOR 1 SERVING:

Calories **387kcal**	Sodium **630mg**
Total Carbohydrates **13g**	Potassium **245mg**
Protein **39g**	Dietary Fiber **3g**
Total Fat **18g**	Sugars **3g**
Saturated Fat **3g**	Vitamin A **6% Daily Value**
Polyunsaturated Fat **10g**	Vitamin C **2% Daily Value**
Monounsaturated Fat **4g**	Calcium **4% Daily Value**
Trans Fat **1g**	Iron **8% Daily Value**
Cholesterol **34mg**	

tarragon, 1 teaspoon lemon rind and the lemon juice. Cook for 2 minutes or until the snap peas are crisp-tender. Serve alongside the salmon fillets.

Grilled Salmon with Tomato-Avocado Salsa

Serves 4

INGREDIENTS

2 cups diced avocado

1 cup halved yellow heirloom cherry tomatoes

2 tbsp. chopped fresh cilantro

½ tsp. chopped serrano chili

1½ tbsp. sliced shallot

1 tsp. fresh lime juice

1 tsp. kosher salt

⅓ tsp. black pepper

1 tbsp. olive oil, divided

4 (6-oz.) salmon fillets, skin on

INSTRUCTIONS

1. Preheat the grill to medium-high (about 450°F).

2. In a medium bowl, combine the avocado, tomatoes, cilantro, serrano chili and shallots. In a small bowl, whisk together the lime juice, ¼ teaspoon of the salt, and ¼ teaspoon of the pepper; drizzle over the avocado mixture and stir to coat.

3. Brush the olive oil on both sides of the salmon, then sprinkle with the remaining ¾ teaspoon salt and ½ teaspoon pepper.

4. Place the salmon, skin side down, on the grill and cook, flipping once, until the salmon is opaque and cooked through, about 3 minutes per side. Serve the salmon topped with the salsa.

NUTRITION · DATA FOR 1 SERVING:

Calories **408kcal**	Sodium **574mg**
Total Carbohydrates **9g**	Potassium **367mg**
Protein **38g**	Dietary Fiber **6g**
Total Fat **24g**	Sugars **1g**
Saturated Fat **4g**	Vitamin A **2% Daily Value**
Polyunsaturated Fat **14g**	Vitamin C **5% Daily Value**
Monounsaturated Fat **5g**	Calcium **3% Daily Value**
Trans Fat **1g**	Iron **7% Daily Value**
Cholesterol **48mg**	

Pasta Salad with Tomatoes and Eggplant

Serves: 4

INGREDIENTS

8 oz. casarecce, fusilli or penne pasta

8 oz. haricots verts (French green beans) or yellow wax beans

1 tbsp. olive oil

2 cups chopped Japanese eggplant (1 eggplant)

1 tbsp. minced garlic

2 pints cherry tomatoes, halved and divided

¼ cup dry white wine

2 tsp. white wine vinegar

½ tsp. kosher salt

6 oz. burrata

2 tsp. chopped fresh thyme

½ tsp. black pepper

INSTRUCTIONS

1. Cook the pasta according to the package instructions, but do not salt the cooking water. Add the green beans during the last 3 minutes of cooking. Reserve 1 cup of the cooking liquid, then drain.

2. Meanwhile, heat the oil in a large skillet over medium-high heat. Add the eggplant and cook, stirring occasionally, until tender, 4 to 5 minutes. Add the garlic and cook until fragrant, 1 minute. Add half of the tomatoes and cook until their juices start to release, 2 to 3 minutes.

3. Add the wine and cook, stirring often, until most of the wine evaporates, about 3-4 minutes. Add the pasta and green beans; toss to combine. If the mixture is too dry, add the reserved pasta cooking liquid a couple of tablespoons at a time. Stir in the remaining tomatoes and the vinegar and salt. Divide the pasta mixture among 4 bowls. Top each bowl evenly with the burrata, thyme and pepper.

NUTRITION · DATA FOR 1 SERVING:

Calories **428kcal**	Sodium **361mg**
Total Carbohydrates **56g**	Potassium **282mg**
Protein **17g**	Dietary Fiber **6g**
Total Fat **14g**	Sugars **9g**
Saturated Fat **7g**	Vitamin A **4% Daily Value**
Polyunsaturated Fat **5g**	Vitamin C **7% Daily Value**
Monounsaturated Fat **2g**	Calcium **28% Daily Value**
Trans Fat **0g**	Iron **13% Daily Value**
Cholesterol **46mg**	

Grilled Heirloom Tomato & Feta Panzanella

Serves: 4

INGREDIENTS

2 lb. heirloom tomatoes, halved

4 oz. French bread, cut into 1-inch slices

¼ cup extra-virgin olive oil, divided

1 (3-oz.) block feta cheese

¼ tsp. kosher salt

¼ tsp. black pepper

1 (14.5-oz.) can unsalted cannellini beans, rinsed and drained

½ cup thinly sliced red onion

½ cup chopped fresh basil leaves

2 tsp. red wine vinegar

INSTRUCTIONS

1. Preheat the grill to 450°F. Brush the tomatoes and bread with 1 tablespoon of the oil. Place the tomatoes, bread and feta cheese directly on the grates and grill until caramelized on both sides, 1 to 2 minutes per side. Transfer to a plate and sprinkle evenly with the salt and pepper. Let cool for 5 minutes, then cut any of the larger tomatoes and the bread slices into chunks.

2. Combine the tomatoes, bread, beans, onion, basil, vinegar and the remaining 3 tablespoons of oil in a large bowl; gently toss. Divide the salad among 4 plates and crumble the feta cheese evenly over the top. Serve immediately.

NUTRITION · DATA FOR 1 SERVING:

Calories **381kcal**	Sodium **530mg**
Total Carbohydrates **39g**	Potassium **436mg**
Protein **13g**	Dietary Fiber **8g**
Total Fat **21g**	Sugars **10g**
Saturated Fat **5g**	Vitamin A **4% Daily Value**
Polyunsaturated Fat **11g**	Vitamin C **9% Daily Value**
Monounsaturated Fat **1g**	Calcium **19% Daily Value**
Trans Fat **3g**	Iron **17% Daily Value**
Cholesterol **46mg**	

Zucchini, Pesto & Sausage Pizza

Makes: 3

INGREDIENTS

3 oz. mild Italian ground turkey sausage

1 cup thinly sliced zucchini

¼ cup basil pesto, divided

1 (12-oz.) package of 3 (7-inch) prebaked pizza crusts

3 oz. fresh mozzarella cheese, very thinly sliced

⅛ tsp. crushed red pepper

2 tbsp. fresh basil leaves

INSTRUCTIONS

1. Preheat the oven to 450°F.

2. Heat a small nonstick skillet over medium-high heat. Add the sausage and cook, stirring and breaking up the sausage with a wooden spoon, until cooked through, 4 to 5 minutes. Transfer the sausage to a plate. Add the zucchini and 1 tablespoon of the pesto to the skillet. Cook, stirring often, until the zucchini is slightly tender, about 3 minutes. Remove from the heat.

3. Place the pizza crusts on a baking sheet and spread the remaining 3 tablespoons of pesto evenly over the crusts. Top each crust evenly with the zucchini mixture, sausage, mozzarella cheese and red pepper. Bake until the crusts are crisped on the edges and the cheese is melted, 7 to 8 minutes. Remove from the oven, and sprinkle evenly with the basil. Cut each pizza into 4 slices and serve immediately.

NUTRITION · DATA FOR 1 SERVING:

Calories **392kcal**	Sodium **782mg**
Total Carbohydrates **44g**	Potassium **576mg**
Protein **15g**	Dietary Fiber **6g**
Total Fat **22g**	Sugars **4g**
Saturated Fat **6g**	Vitamin A **10% Daily Value**
Polyunsaturated Fat **8g**	Vitamin C **8% Daily Value**
Monounsaturated Fat **6g**	Calcium **21% Daily Value**
Trans Fat **2g**	Iron **19% Daily Value**
Cholesterol **60mg**	

Chicken & Cucumber Salad with Parsley Pesto

Serves: 6

INGREDIENTS

2 cups packed, fresh flat-leaf parsley leaves (from 1 bunch)

1 cup fresh baby spinach

2 tbsp. fresh lemon juice

1 tbsp. grated Parmesan cheese

1 tsp. toasted pine nuts

1 medium clove garlic, smashed

1 tsp. kosher salt

¼ tsp. black pepper

½ cup extra virgin olive oil

4 cups shredded rotisserie chicken (from 1 chicken)

2 cups cooked and shelled edamame

1 (15-oz.) can unsalted chickpeas, drained and rinsed

1 cup chopped English cucumber

4 cups loosely packed arugula

INSTRUCTIONS

1. Combine the parsley, spinach, lemon juice, cheese, pine nuts, garlic, salt and pepper in the bowl of a food processor. Process until smooth, about 1 minute. With the processor running, add the oil and process until smooth, about 1 minute longer.

2. Stir together the chicken, edamame, chickpeas and cucumber in a large bowl. Add the pesto and toss to combine.

3. Place ⅔ cup arugula in each of 6 bowls; top each with 1 cup of the chicken salad mixture. Serve immediately.

NUTRITION · DATA FOR 1 SERVING:

Calories **482kcal**	Sodium **465mg**
Total Carbohydrates **22g**	Potassium **345mg**
Protein **40g**	Dietary Fiber **7g**
Total Fat **26g**	Sugars **2g**
Saturated Fat **4g**	Vitamin A **6% Daily Value**
Polyunsaturated Fat **15g**	Vitamin C **12% Daily Value**
Monounsaturated Fat **4g**	Calcium **17% Daily Value**
Trans Fat **3g**	Iron **21% Daily Value**
Cholesterol **46mg**	

Gnocchi with Spinach and Pepper Sauce

Serves: 5

INGREDIENTS

16 oz. whole-wheat potato gnocchi

5 oz. baby spinach

1½ oz. Manchego cheese, grated (about ¼ cup, plus 2 tbsp.), divided

3 tbsp. olive oil, divided

½ cup chopped jarred roasted red peppers

¼ cup smoked almonds

1 chopped plum tomato

1 slice baguette, torn (about ½ oz.)

1 clove garlic

½ tsp. paprika

¼ tsp. crushed red pepper

2 tbsp. sherry vinegar

INSTRUCTIONS

1. Cook the gnocchi according to the package directions, but do not salt the cooking water. Drain and return the gnocchi to the pot. Over medium heat add the spinach, ¼ cup of the cheese and 1 tablespoon of the olive oil. Cover and let stand until the spinach wilts, 2 to 3 minutes. Gently toss to combine evenly.

2. In a food processor, combine the red peppers, almonds, tomato, baguette, garlic, paprika, crushed red pepper, vinegar and remaining 2 tablespoons olive oil and pulse until smooth, about 1 minute.

3. Divide the gnocchi mixture among 5 bowls. Top evenly with the sauce and sprinkle with the remaining 2 tablespoons cheese.

NUTRITION · DATA FOR 1 SERVING:

Calories **324kcal**	Sodium **590mg**
Total Carbohydrates **34g**	Potassium **325mg**
Protein **9g**	Dietary Fiber **8g**
Total Fat **16g**	Sugars **2g**
Saturated Fat **4g**	Vitamin A **8% Daily Value**
Polyunsaturated Fat **7g**	Vitamin C **12% Daily Value**
Monounsaturated Fat **3g**	Calcium **14% Daily Value**
Trans Fat **2g**	Iron **7% Daily Value**
Cholesterol **56mg**	

Chicken & Bulgur Salad with Peaches

Serves: 4

INGREDIENTS

1⅓ cups water

⅔ cup bulgur

1 lb. chicken breast cutlets

1 tsp. kosher salt, divided

½ tsp. black pepper

4 cups packed arugula

2 cups halved cherry tomatoes

2 cups sliced fresh peaches

3 tbsp. extra-virgin olive oil

2 tbsp. rice vinegar

INSTRUCTIONS

1. Combine the water and bulgur in a small saucepan over medium heat and bring to a boil. Lower the heat to medium-low, cover and simmer for 10 minutes. Drain, rinse the bulgur under cold water, then drain again and spread out on paper towels to dry.

2. Meanwhile, coat a grill pan with cooking spray and place over high heat. Sprinkle the chicken with ½ teaspoon of both the salt and the pepper. Transfer to the hot pan and grill, turning occasionally, until done, 6 to 7 minutes. Remove to a cutting board and let stand for 3 minutes, then slice against the grain into strips.

3. Place the bulgur, arugula, tomatoes and peaches in a large bowl. Add the remaining ½ teaspoon salt and the oil and vinegar; toss to coat. Divide the mixture among 4 plates and top evenly with the chicken.

NUTRITION · DATA FOR 1 SERVING:

Calories **364kcal**	Sodium **547mg**
Total Carbohydrates **30g**	Potassium **475mg**
Protein **31g**	Dietary Fiber **6g**
Total Fat **14g**	Sugars **9g**
Saturated Fat **2g**	Vitamin A **5% Daily Value**
Polyunsaturated Fat **6g**	Vitamin C **9% Daily Value**
Monounsaturated Fat **4g**	Calcium **7% Daily Value**
Trans Fat **2g**	Iron **20% Daily Value**
Cholesterol **47mg**	

Almond-Crusted Trout with Swiss Chard

Serves: 4

INGREDIENTS

1⅓ oz. almond flour (about ½ cup)

4 (4-5-oz.) trout fillets, skin on

1 tbsp. Dijon mustard

2½ tbsp. grapeseed oil or canola oil, divided

½ tsp. kosher salt, divided

½ tsp. black pepper, divided

4 cups thinly sliced Swiss chard leaves and stems (about 5 oz.), divided

3 cloves garlic, thinly sliced

¼ cup dry white wine

1 tbsp. fresh lemon juice

1 tbsp. unsalted butter

1 tbsp. minced fresh chives

4 lemon wedges

INSTRUCTIONS

1. Place the almond flour in a shallow bowl. Brush the flesh side of each fish fillet with mustard, then gently press the mustard side of each fillet into the almond flour, leaving the skin side bare. Heat 1 tablespoon of the oil in a large nonstick skillet over medium-high heat. Add 2 fillets, flesh side down, and cook until golden brown and lightly crispy, 2 to 3 minutes.

2. Flip the fillets and cook until the flesh is flaky and the fish is cooked through, about 4–6 minutes. Transfer to a paper towel–lined plate. Wipe the skillet clean, then repeat with another tablespoon of oil and the remaining 2 fillets. Sprinkle the cooked fillets evenly with ¼ teaspoon of the salt and ¼ teaspoon of the pepper.

3. Wipe the skillet clean. Add the remaining 1½ teaspoons oil to the skillet and heat over medium-high heat. Add the chard and cook, stirring occasionally, until slightly tender, 3 to 4 minutes. Add the garlic and cook, stirring often,

recipe continues

NUTRITION · DATA FOR 1 SERVING:

Calories **368kcal**	Sodium **591mg**
Total Carbohydrates **6g**	Potassium **478mg**
Protein **27g**	Dietary Fiber **2g**
Total Fat **25g**	Sugars **1g**
Saturated Fat **5g**	Vitamin A **8% Daily Value**
Polyunsaturated Fat **8g**	Vitamin C **10% Daily Value**
Monounsaturated Fat **6g**	Calcium **17% Daily Value**
Trans Fat **5g**	Iron **9% Daily Value**
Cholesterol **72mg**	

until fragrant, about 1 minute. Add the wine and lemon juice and cook until slightly reduced, about 1 minute. Stir in the butter and season with the remaining ¼ teaspoon salt and ¼ teaspoon pepper. Divide the chard mixture among 4 plates. Top each with a fish fillet and sprinkle over evenly with chives. Serve each plate with a lemon wedge on the side.

Saffron Fish Stew with White Beans

Serves: 4

INGREDIENTS

1 tbsp. extra-virgin olive oil

1 cup chopped onion

2 garlic cloves, crushed

1 sprig thyme

1 tsp. ground fennel

½ tsp. ground coriander

½ tsp. fresh orange peel

¼ tsp. saffron threads

1½ cups water

1½ cups clam juice

1 (14.5-oz.) can diced tomatoes with liquid

1 lb. flounder fillet, cut into 2-inch pieces

1 (14-oz.) can Great Northern beans, rinsed and drained

⅛ tsp. salt

fresh thyme, about 5 leaves

INSTRUCTIONS

1. Heat the oil in a large Dutch oven over medium-high heat. Add the onion, garlic, thyme, fennel and coriander and sauté for 5 minutes. Stir in the orange peel and saffron, then add the water, clam juice and tomatoes.

2. Bring to a boil, then reduce the heat and simmer for 5 minutes. Stir in the fish, beans and salt and cook for 5 minutes more. Divide the stew among 4 bowls and serve topped with the thyme leaves.

NUTRITION · DATA FOR 1 SERVING:

Calories **249kcal**	Sodium **495mg**
Total Carbohydrates **23g**	Potassium **296mg**
Protein **28g**	Dietary Fiber **7g**
Total Fat **5g**	Sugars **1g**
Saturated Fat **3g**	Vitamin A **6% Daily Value**
Polyunsaturated Fat **1g**	Vitamin C **9% Daily Value**
Monounsaturated Fat **2g**	Calcium **15% Daily Value**
Trans Fat **1g**	Iron **22% Daily Value**
Cholesterol **46mg**	

Beef Kofta Patties with Cucumber Salad

Serves: 4

INGREDIENTS

1 lb. ground sirloin

¼ cup, plus 2 tbsp. chopped, fresh flat-leaf parsley, divided

¼ cup chopped fresh cilantro

1 tbsp. chopped fresh ginger

2 tsp. ground coriander

1 tsp. ground cumin

½ tsp. ground cinnamon

½ tsp. salt

2 cups thinly sliced English cucumber

2 tbsp. rice vinegar

½ cup plain, fat-free Greek yogurt

1 tbsp. fresh lemon juice

½ tsp. freshly ground black pepper

2 (6-inch) pitas, quartered

INSTRUCTIONS

1. Heat a grill pan over medium-high heat. Combine the beef, ¼ cup of the parsley, the cilantro, ginger, coriander, cumin, cinnamon and salt in a medium bowl.

2. Divide the beef mixture into 4 equal portions and shape each into a ½-inch-thick patty. Place the patties in the pan and cook for 3 minutes on each side, or to your desired degree of doneness.

3. Meanwhile, in a medium bowl, combine the cucumber and vinegar and toss well. In a small bowl, combine the yogurt, the remaining 2 tablespoons parsley, and the lemon juice and pepper; stir with a whisk. Arrange 1 patty and ½ cup cucumber mixture on each of 4 plates. Top each serving with about 2 tablespoons of the yogurt sauce. Serve each with 2 pita wedges.

NUTRITION · DATA FOR 1 SERVING:

Calories **321kcal**	Sodium **518mg**
Total Carbohydrates **22g**	Potassium **420mg**
Protein **29g**	Dietary Fiber **4g**
Total Fat **12g**	Sugars **4g**
Saturated Fat **5g**	Vitamin A **4% Daily Value**
Polyunsaturated Fat **1g**	Vitamin C **11% Daily Value**
Monounsaturated Fat **3g**	Calcium **25% Daily Value**
Trans Fat **2g**	Iron **14% Daily Value**
Cholesterol **64mg**	

Halibut with Lemon-Fennel Salad

Serves: 4

INGREDIENTS

1 tsp. ground coriander

½ tsp. ground cumin

½ tsp. salt

¼ tsp. freshly ground black pepper

5 tsp. extra virgin olive oil, divided

2 cloves garlic, minced

4 (6-oz.) halibut fillets

2 cups thinly sliced fennel bulb

¼ cup thinly sliced red onion

2 tbsp. fresh lemon juice

1 tbsp. chopped fresh flat-leaf parsley

1 tsp. fresh thyme leaves

INSTRUCTIONS

1. In a small bowl, combine the coriander, cumin, salt and pepper. In a separate small bowl, combine 1½ teaspoons of the spice mixture with 2 teaspoons of the oil and the garlic; rub this garlic mixture evenly over the fish.

2. Heat 1 teaspoon of oil in a large nonstick skillet over medium-high heat. Add the fish and cook for 5 minutes on each side, or to your desired degree of doneness.

3. Meanwhile, combine the remaining ⅓ teaspoon spice mixture and the remaining 2 teaspoons of oil with the fennel, onion, lemon juice, parsley and thyme in a medium bowl, tossing well to coat. Serve the salad alongside the fish.

NUTRITION · DATA FOR 1 SERVING:

Calories **259kcal**	Sodium **780mg**
Total Carbohydrates **5g**	Potassium **356mg**
Protein **36.3g**	Dietary Fiber **5g**
Total Fat **10g**	Sugars **2g**
Saturated Fat **1g**	Vitamin A **6% Daily Value**
Polyunsaturated Fat **3g**	Vitamin C **15% Daily Value**
Monounsaturated Fat **4g**	Calcium **35% Daily Value**
Trans Fat **2g**	Iron **16% Daily Value**
Cholesterol **54mg**	

Italian Meatball Wedding Soup

Serves: 8

INGREDIENTS

For the meatballs:
1 large egg

3 tbsp. finely chopped fresh chives

2 tsp. finely chopped fresh sage

2 cloves garlic, minced

⅓ lb. 85% or 90% lean ground beef

½ lb. sweet or hot Italian sausage, removed from the casings

½ cup grated Parmigiano-Reggiano

⅓ cup Italian-seasoned bread crumbs

¼ tsp. salt

For the soup:
2 tbsp. olive oil

1 medium yellow onion, diced

2 large carrots, diced

2 stalks celery, diced

6 cups high-quality chicken broth, such as Swanson (do not use low-sodium)

2 cups high-quality beef broth, such as Swanson (do not use low-sodium)

2 cups water

INSTRUCTIONS

1. Preheat the oven to 350°F. Line a baking sheet with aluminum foil, then set an ovenproof roasting rack on top. Generously spray the rack with nonstick cooking spray.

2. In a medium bowl, beat the egg together with the chives, sage and garlic. Add all the remaining meatball ingredients and mash with your hands until well combined. Roll the mixture into tablespoon-size balls (about 1 inch in diameter each) and place on the prepared rack. Bake until lightly browned and cooked through, about 18 minutes.

3. Meanwhile, heat the olive oil in a medium soup pot until shimmering. Add the onions, carrots and celery and cook, stirring frequently, until the vegetables are well softened, about 8 minutes. Add the chicken broth, beef broth, water, wine, if using, bay leaf, salt and pepper and bring to a boil for about 8 minutes.

NUTRITION · DATA FOR 1 SERVING:

Calories **359kcal**	Sodium **930mg**
Total Carbohydrates **16g**	Potassium **21mg**
Protein **23g**	Dietary Fiber **2g**
Total Fat **22g**	Sugars **5g**
Saturated Fat **7g**	Vitamin A **10%**
Polyunsaturated Fat **0.5g**	Vitamin C **0%**
Monounsaturated Fat **2g**	Calcium **4%**
Trans Fat **3g**	Iron **3%**
Cholesterol **83mg**	

½ cup dry white wine (optional)

1 bay leaf

½ tsp. salt

¼ tsp. white pepper (or black pepper)

1 cup small pasta, such as ditalini

4 oz. fresh spinach, stems trimmed, roughly chopped (about 3 packed cups)

Parmesan cheese for serving

4. Cook the pasta according to the package directions until al dente, about 7 minutes. Taste the soup and adjust the seasoning if necessary, then lower the heat and add the spinach and meatballs. Simmer for a few minutes, until the spinach is wilted and the meatballs are warmed all the way through. Transfer the soup to bowls and serve with the grated Parmesan cheese.

Caprese Chicken

Serves: 4

INGREDIENTS

2 tbsp. olive oil, divided

2 lb. boneless, skinless chicken breasts

1 tsp. salt

1 tsp. black pepper

1 tsp. chili powder

1 tbsp. dried Italian seasoning

1 tsp. sweet paprika

8 thick slices ripe tomato

8 (1-oz.) slices fresh mozzarella cheese

8 medium basil leaves

4 tbsp. balsamic glaze or balsamic reduction

INSTRUCTIONS

1. Preheat the oven to 350°F.

2. Heat large cast iron pan over medium heat and add 1 tablespoon of the olive oil.

3. While your oil is heating up, butterfly the chicken: cut each chicken breast from the side about three-quarters of the way through, then open the chicken and lay flat.

4. Season each chicken breast with the remaining 1 tablespoon of olive oil, salt, pepper, chili powder, Italian seasoning and sweet paprika.

5. Place 2 slices of tomato, 2 slices of mozzarella cheese and 2 basil leaves on one side of each chicken breast. Close the chicken breasts and use toothpicks to help keep them closed around the filling.

6. Transfer the stuffed chicken breasts to the pan and sear for about 5 minutes on each side, until golden brown.

7. Transfer to the oven until the internal temperature reaches 165°F.

NUTRITION · DATA FOR 1 SERVING:

Calories **366kcal**	Sodium **387mg**
Total Carbohydrates **4g**	Potassium **23mg**
Protein **35g**	Dietary Fiber **1g**
Total Fat **12g**	Sugars **2g**
Saturated Fat **5g**	Vitamin A **35 % Daily Value**
Polyunsaturated fat **3g**	Vitamin C **15 % Daily Value**
Monounsaturated fat **5g**	Calcium **15 % Daily Value**
Trans fat **0g**	Iron **10% Daily Value**
Cholesterol **85mg**	

8. Transfer the chicken breasts to a plate and let rest 3–5 minutes.

9. Slice into ¼-inch slices and drizzle the balsamic glaze over the top of the chicken. Serve over your favorite salad: we suggest the Rustic Avocodo & Corn Salad on page 188.

Rustic Avocado & Corn Salad

Serves: 2

INGREDIENTS

2 avocados, diced

2 medium red onions, diced

2 cups cherry tomatoes

2 cups sweet corn

1 cup feta cheese

2 tbsp. finely chopped fresh cilantro

2 tbsp. finely chopped fresh parsley

2 tbsp. Italian dressing

1 lime, juiced

salt and pepper, to taste

INSTRUCTIONS

1. Arrange the avocado, onion, tomatoes, corn, and feta cheese in 2 medium bowls, giving each ingredient its own section and filling in all the gaps.

2. Sprinkle the cilantro and parsley over the top. Drizzle the dressing and the lime juice over the salad, then season with salt and pepper, to taste.

3. Serve with grilled chicken or salmon, or with our own favorite, the Chicken Caprese on page 186.

NUTRITION · DATA FOR 1 SERVING:

Calories **422kcal**	Sodium **298mg**
Total Carbohydrates **18g**	Potassium **17mg**
Protein **40g**	Dietary Fiber **21g**
Total Fat **29g**	Sugars **9g**
Saturated Fat **8g**	Vitamin A **45%**
Polyunsaturated Fat **18g**	Vitamin C **23%**
Monounsaturated Fat **9g**	Calcium **28%**
Trans Fat **4g**	Iron **22%**
Cholesterol **45mg**	

Chicken Piccata

Serves: 6

INGREDIENTS

2 lbs. (3 large) boneless, skinless chicken breasts

1 tbsp. black pepper

⅓ cup flour

¼ cup olive oil

5 cloves garlic, sliced

¼ cup white wine

¼ cup demi-glace (optional)

1 lemon, juiced

6 lemon slices

½ cup butter

2 tbsp. finely chopped parsley, plus more for garnish

1 tsp. capers

INSTRUCTIONS

1. Slice each chicken breast in half horizontally to make 6 fillets altogether. Gently pound the meat with a mallet until each fillet is thin and flat but not broken. Sprinkle the meat with the black pepper and dredge lightly in the flour.

2. Preheat a wide, heavy skillet over medium heat. Add the olive oil and garlic and sauté until lightly browned, then remove the garlic with a slotted spoon and set aside.

3. Turn the heat up to high and add the chicken. Cook 2–3 minutes per side until golden brown.

4. Remove the chicken to a serving platter and set aside.

5. Drain the oil from the pan, then return the pan to the heat and add the white wine. Cook, stirring, to deglaze the pan for about 1 minute. Add the demi-glace, if using, the lemon juice and the reserved garlic.

recipe continues

NUTRITION · DATA FOR 1 SERVING:

Calories **463kcal**	Sodium **407mg**
Total Carbohydrates **7g**	Potassium **38mg**
Protein **37g**	Dietary Fiber **0.4g**
Total Fat **32g**	Sugars **0.2g**
Saturated Fat **14g**	Vitamin A **12% Daily Value**
Polyunsaturated Fat **2g**	Vitamin C **6% Daily Value**
Monounsaturated Fat **15g**	Calcium **1% Daily Value**
Trans Fat **0g**	Iron **2% Daily Value**
Cholesterol **170mg**	

6. Stir well to heat the sauce thoroughly, then add the butter and stir until fully melted and combined. At this point, you can remove the garlic with a slotted spoon or leave in.

7. Stir in the parsley, then spoon the sauce over the chicken.

8. Garnish with the capers, lemon slices, and more freshly chopped parsley.

Falafel Tortillas with Tahini Sauce

Serves: 6

INGREDIENTS

For the falafel:

1 (24-oz.) can chickpeas, drained and rinsed

1 medium onion, grated

4 scallions, minced

1 bunch parsley, finely chopped

2 tbsp. chopped fresh cilantro

1 tsp. garlic, chopped

2 tsp. ground coriander

2 tsp. ground cumin

½ tsp. baking powder

2–3 cups canola oil, for deep frying

For the Tahini Sauce:

⅔ cup tahini (sesame paste)

3 tbsp. tater, plus more as needed

2 lemons, juiced

2 cloves garlic, minced

2 tbsp. minced fresh parsley

1 tsp. black pepper

To serve:

6 medium/large tortillas or pita breads, warmed

1½ cups mixed lettuce leaves

INSTRUCTIONS

1. To make the batter, remove the skins from the chickpeas by rubbing them with a dish towel.

2. Place the skinned chickpeas in the bowl of a food processor and purée. Add the onions, scallions, parsley, cilantro, garlic, coriander, cumin and baking powder. Blend the ingredients together until a smooth paste forms (add a little water if necessary).

3. Let the mixture rest for 30 minutes.

4. Meanwhile, make the tahini sauce. In a small bowl combine the tahini, water and lemon juice. Mix together to form a smooth sauce, adding more water if necessary.

5. Add the garlic, parsley and black pepper and mix until well blended. Set the sauce aside.

6. To fry the falafel, fill a medium to large saucepan or pot with enough oil, about ¼ inch, for deep frying and place over medium-high heat.

recipe continues

NUTRITION · DATA FOR 1 SERVING:	
Calories **668kcal**	Sodium **707mg**
Total Carbohydrates **61g**	Potassium **466mg**
Protein **16g**	Dietary Fiber **12g**
Total Fat **42g**	Sugars **3g**
Saturated Fat **6g**	Vitamin A **20% Daily Value**
Polyunsaturated Fat **13g**	Vitamin C **38% Daily Value**
Monounsaturated Fat **8g**	Calcium **18% Daily Value**
Trans Fat **0g**	Iron **31% Daily Value**
Cholesterol **0mg**	

1½ cups halved cherry tomatoes

6 lemon wedges

7. When the oil is hot, use a small, 1 oz. (½-inch) ice cream scoop to scoop the falafel mixture into balls and drop each one into the hot oil, working in batches if necessary. Deep-fry each batch for 2 to 3 minutes, or until the falafel are golden brown.

8. Remove from the oil with a slotted spoon and set on a paper towel–lined plate to drain. Repeat to fry the remaining batter.

9. To serve, set the falafel, tahini sauce, and other fixings on the table and allow your guests to assemble their own tortillas. Set a tortilla down and add a bed of lettuce, then top with cherry tomatoes and falafel. Squeeze over some lemon juice and top with the tahini sauce, fold and enjoy.

Fish in Island Sauce

Serves: 6

INGREDIENTS

3 tbsp. olive oil

6 cloves garlic, minced

6 grouper or other white-fleshed fish fillets (3 lbs.)

2 onions, peeled and diced

1 can (15 oz.) diced tomatoes, drained

1 green bell pepper, seeded and diced

½ cup drained capers

2 tbsp. finely chopped parsley

2 tbsp. white wine vinegar

1 bay leaf

INSTRUCTIONS

1. Heat the oil in a large skillet over medium-high heat. Add the garlic and cook until golden, about 2 minutes.

2. Add the fish fillets and fry, turning once, until golden and cooked through and the fish flakes easily with a fork, approximately 3 minutes on each side.

3. Remove the fish from the skillet, cover to keep warm and set aside.

4. Add the onion to the skillet and sauté until transparent, about 5 minutes.

5. Mix the tomatoes and bell pepper and continue to sauté for another 5 to 6 minutes.

6. Add the capers, parsley, vinegar and bay leaf. Bring to a boil and cook for another 10 minutes.

7. Place a fish fillet on each plate, pour the sauce over the fish and serve immediately.

NUTRITION · DATA FOR 1 SERVING:

Calories **223kcal**	Sodium **696mg**
Total Carbohydrates **10g**	Potassium **235mg**
Protein **26g**	Dietary Fiber **2g**
Total Fat **9g**	Sugars **4g**
Saturated Fat **1g**	Vitamin A **16% Daily Value**
Polyunsaturated Fat **1g**	Vitamin C **55% Daily Value**
Monounsaturated Fat **5g**	Calcium **7% Daily Value**
Trans Fat **0.4g**	Iron **13% Daily Value**
Cholesterol **61mg**	

Fregola with Clams & Chilies

Serves: 6

INGREDIENTS

1 lb. fregola

¼ cup olive oil

1 medium red onion, peeled and thinly sliced

4 cloves garlic, peeled and thinly sliced

2 oz. prosciutto, diced into ⅛-inch pieces

1 lb. tiny clams (such as Manilas), cockles or mussels, scrubbed and rinsed

1 cup dry white wine

1 cup chicken stock

½ cup tomato purée

1 pinch saffron

1 tbsp. crushed red pepper

salt and black pepper, to taste

1 bunch Italian parsley, leaves only

INSTRUCTIONS

1. Cook the fregola according to the package instructions until just cooked, approximately 15 minutes.

2. Meanwhile, in a medium saucepan, heat the olive oil to smoking over medium-high heat.

3. Add the onion, garlic and prosciutto and sauté until softened, about 5–8 minutes.

4. Add the clams, white wine, chicken stock, tomato purée and saffron and bring to a boil. Cover and cook 5–8 minutes, until most of the clams have opened. Discard any that haven't opened.

5. Add the cooked fregola to the clams and cook 3-5 minutes longer until the texture resembles risotto.

6. Add the crushed red pepper and stir to combine.

7. Season with salt and black pepper, to taste, garnish with a generous amount of parsley and serve immediately.

NUTRITION · DATA FOR 1 SERVING:

Calories **511kcal**	Sodium **451mg**
Total Carbohydrates **68g**	Potassium **584mg**
Protein **23g**	Dietary Fiber **5g**
Total Fat **13g**	Sugars **4g**
Saturated Fat **2g**	Vitamin A **16% Daily Value**
Polyunsaturated Fat **2g**	Vitamin C **31% Daily Value**
Monounsaturated Fat **8g**	Calcium **3% Daily Value**
Trans Fat **0.2g**	Iron **69% Daily Value**
Cholesterol **31mg**	

Meat Loaf Stuffed with Prosciutto & Cheese

Serves: 6

INGREDIENTS

For the meat loaf:
1¼ lb. ground beef

1 large onion, finely chopped

1 green bell pepper, seeded and finely chopped

1 cup bread crumbs, plus more as needed

2 tbsp. chopped fresh parsley

1 clove garlic, minced

1 (10.75-oz.) can tomato soup

2 large eggs, lightly beaten

1 tsp. prepared mustard, preferably Dijon

½ tsp. dried oregano

⅛ tsp. salt

⅛ tsp. black pepper

For the stuffing:
6–8 slices prosciutto

1 cup shredded mozzarella cheese

INSTRUCTIONS

1. Preheat the oven to 375°F. Lightly oil a 9-by-5-inch pan.

2. In a large bowl, combine all the meat loaf ingredients and mix with your hands until well combined. Add more bread crumbs if necessary, one tablespoon at a time, until the mixture is firm enough to shape into a loaf.

3. Lightly spray a large piece of aluminum foil or nonstick baking paper. Turn the meat mixture out onto the foil and form it into a 12-by-8-inch rectangle.

4. Arrange the prosciutto on top of the meat, leaving a small margin around the edges. Sprinkle the shredded mozzarella cheese on top of the prosciutto slices.

recipe continues

NUTRITION · DATA FOR 1 SERVING:

Calories **446kcal**	Sodium **990mg**
Total Carbohydrates **28g**	Potassium **758mg**
Protein **32g**	Dietary Fiber **3g**
Total Fat **22g**	Sugars **8g**
Saturated Fat **9g**	Vitamin A **20% Daily Value**
Polyunsaturated Fat **1g**	Vitamin C **62% Daily Value**
Monounsaturated Fat **8g**	Calcium **20% Daily Value**
Trans Fat **1g**	Iron **25% Daily Value**
Cholesterol **153mg**	

5. Starting from the short end, carefully roll the meat mixture jelly-roll style. Seal the edges and ends by pressing and pinch the meat loaf together at the ends and along the seam. Place the loaf seam side up in the prepared pan.

6. Bake for 1 hour or until it reaches an internal temperature of 165°F.

7. Serve with your choice of steamed vegetables or side salad.

Mediterranean Meatballs

Serves: 6

INGREDIENTS

For the sauce:

3 tbsp. olive oil

2 cloves garlic, minced

2 onions, peeled and diced

2 green peppers, seeded and diced

2 zucchini, diced

1 large eggplant, peeled and cubed

4 tomatoes, peeled and chopped

¼ cup freshly chopped parsley

½ tsp. dried thyme

½ cup chicken stock

salt and black pepper, to taste

For the meatballs:

2 slices white or whole-wheat bread

1½ lb. ground beef

⅓ cup Parmesan cheese

¼ tsp. nutmeg

2 tsp. salt

2 tsp. black pepper

1 egg, lightly beaten

2–4 tbsp. olive oil

INSTRUCTIONS

1. To make the sauce, heat the olive oil in a large skillet or saucepan over medium-high heat. Add the garlic and sauté until the garlic starts to brown.

2. Add the onion and continue to sauté until translucent.

3. Add the green peppers, zucchini, eggplant and tomatoes. Continue to cook for 7 minutes, then add the parsley, thyme, chicken stock and salt and pepper, to taste. Reduce the heat and allow to simmer, uncovered, for approximately 40 minutes to make a thick sauce.

4. Meanwhile, make the meatballs. Place the bread in the bowl of a food processor and pulse a few times until it resembles crumbs; set aside.

5. In a large bowl mix the ground meat with the Parmesan cheese, nutmeg, and salt and pepper, to taste.

6. Roll the meat mixture into balls about 1 inch wide. Dip each ball into the beaten egg and then into the bread crumbs; set the coated balls aside.

recipe continues

NUTRITION · DATA FOR 1 SERVING:

Calories **555kcal**	Sodium **328mg**
Total Carbohydrates **43g**	Potassium **1072mg**
Protein **33g**	Dietary Fiber **7g**
Total Fat **28g**	Sugars **8g**
Saturated Fat **9g**	Vitamin A **25% Daily Value**
Polyunsaturated Fat **2g**	Vitamin C **94% Daily Value**
Monounsaturated Fat **14g**	Calcium **17% Daily Value**
Trans Fat **1g**	Iron **26% Daily Value**
Cholesterol **115mg**	

To serve:

1 cup cooked spaghetti (or other pasta of choice)

Parmesan cheese

chopped fresh parsley

7. Heat the olive oil in a large skillet over medium-high heat. Add the meatballs and fry on each side 6–8 minutes until golden brown. Remove the cooked meatballs from the pan, drop into the sauce, and gently stir.

8. Serve the meatballs and sauce over the cooked spaghetti. Sprinkle with more Parmesan cheese if desired, and garnish with fresh parsley.

Neapolitan Polenta Pie

Serves: 4

INGREDIENTS

12 oz. plain Greek yogurt

1 tsp. sea salt, divided

3 cups water

1 cup polenta

1½ cups pizza sauce

1 cup thinly sliced red onion

1 tomato, sliced

1 cup sliced green bell pepper

¼ lb. wild mushrooms, washed and sliced

2 oz. dried porcini mushrooms, soaked and drained

3 tbsp. capers

⅓ cup grated Parmesan cheese

⅓ cup chopped fresh basil

INSTRUCTIONS

1. The day before serving, prepare the yogurt "cheese." Mix the yogurt with ½ teaspoon of the salt in a small bowl. Line a strainer with several layers of cheesecloth, then transfer the yogurt to the strainer.

2. Squeeze the cloth very gently around the yogurt and place the strainer over a bowl. Refrigerate and let drain for at least 10 hours.

3. When ready to continue with the recipe, carefully remove the cheesecloth from the ball of cheese. Preheat the oven to 425°F.

4. Bring the water to a boil in a saucepan and stir the polenta into the boiling water.

5. Add remaining ½ teaspoon salt, then reduce the heat to low, cover, and cook, stirring frequently, for 15 minutes or until thick and soft.

6. Pour the polenta into a 9-inch nonstick pie plate or casserole dish and spread evenly over the bottom and up the sides.

7. Spread the pizza sauce over the polenta.

recipe continues

NUTRITION · DATA FOR 1 SERVING:

Calories **272kcal**	Sodium **1412mg**
Total Carbohydrates **35g**	Potassium **749mg**
Protein **18g**	Dietary Fiber **9g**
Total Fat **7g**	Sugars **13g**
Saturated Fat **4g**	Vitamin A **52% Daily Value**
Polyunsaturated Fat **1g**	Vitamin C **192% Daily Value**
Monounsaturated Fat **1g**	Calcium **18% Daily Value**
Trans Fat **1g**	Iron **31% Daily Value**
Cholesterol **23mg**	

8. Arrange the onion, tomato, bell pepper, and mushrooms over the sauce, then top with the yogurt "cheese," capers and Parmesan cheese. Bake for 25 minutes or until the pie is bubbling hot throughout.

9. Remove from the oven and top with the basil before slicing and serving.

Portuguese Chorizo Soup

Serves: 6

INGREDIENTS

2 tbsp. olive oil

1 cup diced onion

2 tsp. minced garlic

8 oz. chorizo sausage, thinly sliced

2 cups peeled, sliced potatoes

4 cups chicken stock

4 cups water

½ lb. kale, stemmed and sliced

½ lb. green beans, trimmed and sliced

salt and pepper, to taste

INSTRUCTIONS

1. Heat the olive oil in a medium to large soup pot over medium heat. Add the onions and garlic and cook 2–3 minutes, until soft and transparent (don't allow them to brown).

2. Add the chorizo and potatoes and sauté for 5 to10 minutes more, or until the potatoes are slightly golden and the sausage is browned.

3. Pour in the stock and water and bring to a boil. Cook at a gentle boil over medium heat for 15 minutes.

4. Add the kale and green beans, reduce the heat to low, and simmer, uncovered, for 5 minutes.

5. Season with salt and pepper, to taste, and ladle into bowls and serve.

NUTRITION · DATA FOR 1 SERVING:

Calories **309kcal**	Sodium **899mg**
Total Carbohydrates **28g**	Potassium **692mg**
Protein **12g**	Dietary Fiber **6g**
Total Fat **17g**	Sugars **3g**
Saturated Fat **5g**	Vitamin A **132% Daily Value**
Polyunsaturated Fat **1g**	Vitamin C **122% Daily Value**
Monounsaturated Fat **4g**	Calcium **13% Daily Value**
Trans Fat **0.8g**	Iron **15% Daily Value**
Cholesterol **23mg**	

Roasted Lamb Rack with Velvet-Black Olive Sauce

Serves: 4

INGREDIENTS

For the sauce:
½ cup unsalted butter

4 cloves garlic, peeled and crushed

4 shallots, peeled and chopped

1 tbsp. black peppercorns

2 cups Madeira wine

2 cups red wine

1 medium tomato, diced

1 small rosemary sprig

1 cup demi-glace (or good-quality lamb or beef broth)

½ cup pitted Niçoise olives

salt and pepper, to taste

For the lamb:
2 lamb racks, 8 chops on each

1 tbsp. olive oil, plus more for the pan

2 tsp. salt

2 tsp. black pepper

1 rosemary sprig, leaves only, chopped

INSTRUCTIONS

1. Preheat the oven to 350°F.

For the sauce:

2. To make the sauce, heat 1 tablespoon of the butter in a large skillet over medium heat. Add the garlic, shallots and peppercorns and sauté until lightly browned.

3. Add the Madeira, red wine, tomato and rosemary.

4. Simmer until reduced by two-thirds, leaving approximately 1 cup total, about 30 minutes.

5. Add the demi-glace and bring to a boil. Whisk in the remaining butter a little at a time until it is incorporated. (If you would like a thicker, richer sauce, simply add a little more butter.)

6. Strain the sauce through a fine-mesh strainer, then transfer to a blender.

7. Add half the olives and purée until almost smooth.

NUTRITION · DATA FOR 1 SERVING:

Calories **1247kcal**	Sodium **1656mg**
Total Carbohydrates **29g**	Potassium **384mg**
Protein **88g**	Dietary Fiber **1g**
Total Fat **61g**	Sugars **12g**
Saturated Fat **26g**	Vitamin A **22% Daily Value**
Polyunsaturated Fat **4g**	Vitamin C **12% Daily Value**
Monounsaturated Fat **23g**	Calcium **9% Daily Value**
Trans Fat **0.5g**	Iron **44% Daily Value**
Cholesterol **340mg**	

8. Roughly chop the remaining olives, add to the sauce and stir to mix.

9. Season with salt and pepper, to taste, then set aside in a warm place until serving time.

For the lamb:

10. To make the lamb, rub each rack well with the olive oil and season with the salt, pepper and rosemary.

11. Heat a roasting pan or large sauté pan over high heat until very hot.

12. Add a few drops of oil to the pan, then add the lamb racks and sear on all sides until brown.

13. Turn the racks bone side down in the hot pan and transfer to the oven. Roast to your desired doneness, 10–15 minutes for medium-rare.

14. Allow the lamb to rest for 10 minutes, then slice into 8 chops per rack.

15. Serve 4 chops on each plate, accompanied by the sauce. We suggest serving these with garlic-mashed potatoes and lightly cooked vegetables.

Stuffed Baked Squid

Serves: 4

INGREDIENTS

4 large fresh large squid (about 3 lb.)

¼ cup olive oil

1 cup coarsely chopped onion

⅓ cup long-grain rice

⅓ cup pine nuts

2 large cloves garlic, chopped

¼ cup currants

1 cup dry red wine

¼ cup water, plus more as needed

salt and freshly ground black pepper, to taste

¾ cup chopped fresh parsley

¼ cup chopped fresh dill

¼ cup chopped fresh mint

2 cups canned diced tomatoes

INSTRUCTIONS

1. Preheat the oven to 350°F.

2. Wash and clean each squid. Grasp the head just below the eyes and pull it off from the rest of the body; set aside.

3. Cut away the thin purplish membrane on the outside of the tail section. Using your index finger, scoop out and discard the guts and thin cartilage "icicle" on the inside of the tail section. Rinse the tail sections inside and out and set aside in a colander to drain.

4. Take the head section in one hand and put pressure with your thumb and forefinger around the mouth and eyes to squeeze them out. Discard the mouth and eyes.

5. Chop the squid tentacles and set aside. These will be used in the stuffing.

6. Heat 2 tablespoons of the olive oil in a large skillet over medium heat. Add the onion and sauté until soft, about 5–6 minutes.

7. Add the rice, tentacles and pine nuts and sauté 2–3 minutes

---

NUTRITION · DATA FOR 1 SERVING:

Calories **558kcal**	Sodium **323mg**
Total Carbohydrates **25g**	Potassium **1074mg**
Protein **43g**	Dietary Fiber **3g**
Total Fat **26g**	Sugars **6g**
Saturated Fat **4g**	Vitamin A **17% Daily Value**
Polyunsaturated Fat **7g**	Vitamin C **57% Daily Value**
Monounsaturated Fat **13g**	Calcium **13% Daily Value**
Trans Fat **0.8g**	Iron **21% Daily Value**
Cholesterol **583mg**	

8. Add the garlic and currants and stir quickly with a wooden spoon.

9. Pour in ¼ cup of the wine and ¼ cup of the water. Season with salt and pepper, to taste. Reduce the heat to low and simmer, covered, for about 10 minutes, then add the parsley, dill and mint. Cover and continue to cook about 5 minutes more, until the liquid is almost completely absorbed and the rice is soft but only about half cooked. Remove from the heat and let cool.

10. When the rice is cool enough to handle, use a small teaspoon or a butter knife to carefully fill about three-quarters of each squid with the rice mixture.

11. Use toothpicks to hold the squid securely closed.

12. Pour the remaining 2 tablespoons olive oil into a large casserole dish.

13. Place the squid carefully in the dish and pour in the remaining ¾ cup wine and the canned tomatoes. If the squid are not fully submerged, add just enough water to cover, then season with salt and pepper, to taste.

14. Cover and place in the oven to cook for 1½ to 2 hours or until the rice is cooked and the squid is fork-tender.

15. Check throughout the cooking time to see if more water is necessary so that the mixture doesn't dry out.

16. Serve the squid with a simple green salad.

Turkey Barley Soup

Serves: 4

INGREDIENTS

8 cups chicken stock

1½ cups diced cooked turkey breast

1 cup pearl barley

1 onion, chopped

2 stalks celery, chopped

3 carrots, sliced

1 bay leaf

1 tsp. dry thyme

¼ tsp. dried marjoram

¼ tsp. ground black pepper

2 tbsp. chopped fresh parsley

salt and pepper, to taste

INSTRUCTIONS

1. Combine all the ingredients in a large soup pot over medium heat or in a slow cooker.

2. Cook in the slow cooker on low for 6 hours, or simmer on the stove covered for 1 hour, until the carrots are tender and the barley is soft.

3. Ladle the soup into four serving bowls, season with salt and pepper, to taste, and serve with warm crusty bread if desired.

NUTRITION · DATA FOR 1 SERVING:

Calories **294kcal**	Sodium **81mg**
Total Carbohydrates **51g**	Potassium **632mg**
Protein **19g**	Dietary Fiber **10g**
Total Fat **3g**	Sugars **5g**
Saturated Fat **0.4g**	Vitamin A **172% Daily Value**
Polyunsaturated Fat **0.3g**	Vitamin C **11% Daily Value**
Monounsaturated Fat **0.3g**	Calcium **6% Daily Value**
Trans Fat **0.3g**	Iron **14% Daily Value**
Cholesterol **32mg**	

Tuscan White Bean Stew

Serves: 6

INGREDIENTS

1 tbsp. olive oil

2 anchovy fillets, chopped

1 tsp. minced garlic

½ tsp. paprika

½ tsp. crushed red pepper

1 cup shredded or diced cabbage

1 large green bell pepper, seeded and chopped

1 (14-oz.) can crushed tomatoes

1½ cups canned white beans, drained and rinsed

1 cup chicken broth

2 tsp. freshly squeezed lemon juice

4 oz. pasta (such as farfalle)

salt and pepper, to taste

freshly chopped oregano

freshly chopped parsley

INSTRUCTIONS

1. Heat the oil in a large saucepan over medium-high heat.

2. Stir in the anchovies, garlic, paprika and crushed red pepper and heat for approximately 30 seconds.

3. Add the cabbage and bell pepper and sauté for another 1 to 2 minutes until the cabbage is slightly limp.

4. Add the crushed tomatoes, beans, broth and lemon juice.

5. Reduce the heat to medium-low and allow to simmer, uncovered, 10–15 minutes.

6. Meanwhile, cook the pasta according to the package directions.

7. Divide the hot pasta among 6 bowls and spoon the stew over the top. Season with salt and black pepper to taste. Garnish with chopped oregano and parsley.

NUTRITION · DATA FOR 1 SERVING:

Calories **168kcal**		Sodium **539mg**	
Total Carbohydrates **27g**		Potassium **312mg**	
Protein **9g**		Dietary Fiber **7g**	
Total Fat **3g**		Sugars **1g**	
Saturated Fat **1g**		Vitamin A **14% Daily Value**	
Polyunsaturated Fat **1g**		Vitamin C **55% Daily Value**	
Monounsaturated Fat **2g**		Calcium **10% Daily Value**	
Trans Fat **3g**		Iron **18% Daily Value**	
Cholesterol **3mg**			

Drink
RECIPES

Sun Smoothie

Serves: 1

INGREDIENTS

1 cup almond milk

½ cup orange juice

¼ cup wheat germ

1 banana

INSTRUCTIONS

Combine all four ingredients in a blender. Blend on high until smooth. Serve immediately.

NUTRITION · DATA FOR 1 SERVING:

Calories **140kcal**	Sodium **5mg**
Total Carbohydrates **98g**	Potassium **2mg**
Protein **2g**	Dietary Fiber **4g**
Total Fat **0g**	Sugars **85g**
Saturated Fat **0g**	Vitamin A **5% Daily Value**
Polyunsaturated Fat **0g**	Vitamin C **9.4% Daily Value**
Monounsaturated Fat **0g**	Calcium **2.6% Daily Value**
Trans Fat **0g**	Iron **3.8% Daily Value**
Cholesterol **0mg**	

Frosty Fruit Smoothie

Serves: 1

INGREDIENTS

1 banana

1 cup frozen strawberries

1 cup orange juice

mint leaf (optional)

INSTRUCTIONS

Combine all the ingredients into a blender and purée on high speed. Serve immediately, topped with a mint leaf, if desired.

NUTRITION · DATA FOR 1 SERVING:

Calories **120kcal**	Sodium **15mg**
Total Carbohydrates **28.8g**	Potassium **8mg**
Protein **1.4g**	Dietary Fiber **0g**
Total Fat **0g**	Sugars **27g**
Saturated Fat **0g**	Vitamin A **10% Daily Value**
Polyunsaturated Fat **0g**	Vitamin C **6.3% Daily Value**
Monounsaturated Fat **0g**	Calcium **2.4% Daily Value**
Trans Fat **0g**	Iron **1.8% Daily Value**
Cholesterol **0mg**	

Sugar-Free Blueberry Lemonade

Serves: 3

INGREDIENTS

1½ cups fresh lemon juice

½ cup powdered stevia (sugar substitute)

6 cups water

1 cup cold sparkling water

1 cup blueberries, plus more for garnish

¼ cup mixed fresh herbs, such as basil, mint and tarragon, plus more for garnish

INSTRUCTIONS

Pour the lemon juice into a pitcher and stir in the stevia until dissolved. Add the water and sparkling water and stir well. Mash the blueberries and herbs in a bowl with a wooden spoon. Divide the blueberry mixture among 3 or 4 cups and pour the lemonade over the top. Garnish each glass with whole blueberries and mint.

NUTRITION · DATA FOR 1 SERVING:

Calories **110kcal**	Sodium **50mg**
Total Carbohydrates **2.8g**	Potassium **29mg**
Protein **21.4g**	Dietary Fiber **1g**
Total Fat **0g**	Sugars **0g**
Saturated Fat **0g**	Vitamin A **3.4% Daily Value**
Polyunsaturated Fat **0g**	Vitamin C **5.2% Daily Value**
Monounsaturated Fat **0g**	Calcium **3.6% Daily Value**
Trans Fat **0g**	Iron **8.3% Daily Value**
Cholesterol **0mg**	

Greek Yogurt Smoothie

Serves: 2

INGREDIENTS

⅓ cup Greek yogurt

½ ripe banana, frozen

⅓ cup blueberries, frozen, plus more for garnish

½ cup spinach, frozen

¼ cup almond milk

mint leaves (optional)

INSTRUCTIONS

Combine all the ingredients in a blender and blend until smooth and creamy. Serve immediately, garnished with extra berries and a sprig of mint, if desired.

NUTRITION · DATA FOR 1 SERVING:

Calories **280kcal**	Sodium **90mg**
Total Carbohydrates **1g**	Potassium **65mg**
Protein **12g**	Dietary Fiber **4g**
Total Fat **1g**	Sugars **22g**
Saturated Fat **0.4g**	Vitamin A **6.3% Daily Value**
Polyunsaturated Fat **0.1g**	Vitamin C **2.8% Daily Value**
Monounsaturated Fat **0.3g**	Calcium **4.6% Daily Value**
Trans Fat **0.1g**	Iron **5.7% Daily Value**
Cholesterol **10mg**	

Date Horchata

Serves: 6

INGREDIENTS

6 cups water

1 cup white rice

½ cup dates

1½ tsp. vanilla extract

1 cinnamon stick

1 tbsp. maple syrup (optional)

1 cup almond milk

INSTRUCTIONS

1. Heat 2 cups of the water until it is hot, but not quite boiling. Add the rice and soak in the hot water for 2 hours. The rice should be soft, but still raw. Drain and transfer the rice to a blender. Add the remaining 4 cups of water, the dates, vanilla and cinnamon. Blend for about 1 minute. Test for sweetness, and add more dates or maple syrup as needed.

2. Pour the mixture through a cheesecloth into a bowl; discard the pulp. Stir in the almond milk and whisk until well combined. Transfer to a serving pitcher. Serve immediately over ice.

NUTRITION · DATA FOR 1 SERVING:

Calories **83kcal**	Sodium **75mg**
Total Carbohydrates **20g**	Potassium **38mg**
Protein **1g**	Dietary Fiber **4g**
Total Fat **2g**	Sugars **2g**
Saturated Fat **1g**	Vitamin A **5.2% Daily Value**
Polyunsaturated Fat **1g**	Vitamin C **4.8% Daily Value**
Monounsaturated Fat **1g**	Calcium **6.8 % Daily Value**
Trans Fat **1g**	Iron **3.7% Daily Value**
Cholesterol **0mg**	

Snack
RECIPES

Greek Spinach Pie (Spanakopita)

Makes: 1 Pie (12 slices)

INGREDIENTS

For the filling:

16 oz. frozen chopped spinach, thawed and well drained

2 bunches flat-leaf parsley, stems trimmed, finely chopped

1 large yellow onion, finely chopped

2 cloves, minced

10.5 oz. feta cheese, crumbled

4 eggs

2 tbsp. extra-virgin olive oil

2 tsp. dried dill weed

freshly ground black pepper

For the crust:

1 (16-oz.) package Phyllo pastry, thawed according to package directions

1 cup extra-virgin olive oil, or more if needed

INSTRUCTIONS

1. Preheat the oven to 325°F.

2. Drain the spinach well and squeeze out any excess liquid with your hands, then transfer to a medium bowl.

3. Add all the remaining filling ingredients and stir until well combined.

4. Unroll the phyllo sheets and place them between two slightly damp kitchen cloths.

5. Brush the bottom and sides of a 9½-by-13-inch baking dish with the olive oil.

6. Line the baking dish with two sheets of phyllo, allowing them to cover the sides of the dish. Brush with more olive oil. Add two more sheets of phyllo, and brush them with olive oil. Repeat until two-thirds of the phyllo have been used up.

recipe continues

NUTRITION · DATA FOR 1 SERVING:

Calories **393kcal**	Sodium **290mg**
Total Carbohydrates **38g**	Potassium **141mg**
Protein **21g**	Dietary Fiber **1g**
Total Fat **20g**	Sugars **0g**
Saturated Fat **3g**	Vitamin A **8% Daily Value**
Trans Fat **0g**	Vitamin C **5% Daily Value**
Polyunsaturated Fat **2g**	Calcium **36% Daily Value**
Monounsaturated Fat **3g**	Iron **3% Daily Value**
Cholesterol **35mg**	

7. Next, evenly distribute the spinach and feta filling over the phyllo. Top with two more sheets, and brush with olive oil.

8. Continue to layer the phyllo sheets two at a time, brushing with olive oil, until you've used up all the sheets. Brush the very top layer with olive oil, and sprinkle with just a few drops of water.

9. Fold the flaps (if necessary) and remove excess from the sides—you can crumble them a little. Brush the folded sides well with olive oil.

10. Bake for 1 hour, or until the phyllo crust is crisp and golden brown. Remove from the oven. Let stand for 5 minutes, then cut into squares and serve.

Classic Lemon Hummus

Serves: 8

INGREDIENTS

3 cups cooked, peeled chickpeas

1–2 cloves garlic, minced

3–4 ice cubes

⅓ cup tahini paste

½ tsp. kosher salt

1 lemon, juiced

hot water (if needed)

early-harvest, extra-virgin olive oil

ground sumac powder, to taste

INSTRUCTIONS

1. Combine the chickpeas and garlic in the bowl of a food processor. Purée until a smooth, powderlike mixture forms.

2. With the processor running, add the ice cubes, tahini paste, salt and lemon juice. Blend for about 4 minutes. If the consistency is still too thick, slowly add a little hot water with the processor running, and blend until you reach the desired silky-smooth consistency.

3. Spread the hummus into a serving bowl and add a generous drizzle of oil. Place a few chickpeas in the middle, if preferred. Sprinkle the sumac powder on top. Enjoy with warm pita wedges and your favorite vegetables. Store in the refrigerator for up to 5 days, if desired.

NUTRITION · DATA FOR 1 SERVING:

Calories **176kcal**	Sodium **153mg**
Total Carbohydrates **19g**	Potassium **74mg**
Protein **7g**	Dietary Fiber **0.9g**
Total Fat **9g**	Sugars **3g**
Saturated Fat **4g**	Vitamin A **4% Daily Value**
Monounsaturated Fat **1g**	Vitamin C **6% Daily Value**
Polyunsaturated Fat **0.7g**	Calcium **17% Daily Value**
Trans Fat **3g**	Iron **13% Daily Value**
Cholesterol **0.0mg**	

Smooth Tzatziki

Serves: 3

INGREDIENTS

⅓ English cucumber, partially peeled (striped) and sliced

1 tsp. kosher salt, divided

4 to 5 cloves garlic, peeled and finely grated or minced (you can use less if you prefer)

1 tbsp. extra-virgin olive oil, plus more for serving

1 tsp. white vinegar

2 cups Greek yogurt

¼ tsp. ground white pepper

INSTRUCTIONS

1. Grate the cucumbers in a food processor, then toss with ½ teaspoon of the salt. Transfer to a fine-mesh strainer over a deep bowl to drain, about 10 minutes. Spoon the grated cucumber into a piece of cheesecloth or a double-thickness napkin and squeeze dry. Set aside.

2. In a large mixing bowl, combine the garlic with the remaining ½ teaspoon of salt, the olive oil and the vinegar. Mix to combine evenly.

3. Add the grated cucumber to the large bowl with the garlic mixture. Stir in the yogurt and white pepper. Combine thoroughly, then cover tightly and refrigerate for a couple of hours.

4. When ready to serve, stir the tzatziki to refresh and transfer to a serving bowl. Drizzle with more extra-virgin olive oil, if desired. Add a side of warm pita bread and your favorite vegetables. Enjoy!

NUTRITION · DATA FOR 1 SERVING:

Calories **34kcal**	Sodium **209mg**
Total Carbohydrates **1g**	Potassium **156mg**
Protein **1g**	Dietary Fiber **1g**
Fat **1g**	Sugars **1g**
Saturated Fat **1g**	Vitamin A **9% Daily Value**
Polyunsaturated Fat **1g**	Vitamin C **11% Daily Value**
Monounsaturated Fat **1g**	Calcium **29% Daily Value**
Trans Fat **01g**	Iron **10% Daily Value**
Cholesterol **10mg**	

Tahini Sauce

Serves: 5

INGREDIENTS

1-2 cloves garlic

½ tsp. salt

⅓ cup tahini paste

½ cup freshly squeezed lime juice (or lemon juice, if you prefer)

1 cup chopped fresh parsley leaves (optional)

INSTRUCTIONS

1. Using a mortar and pestle, crush the garlic cloves with the salt into a paste. Alternatively, you can mince the garlic, and season with salt.

2. Add the crushed garlic, tahini paste and lime juice to the bowl of a food processor and blend (it will become thick as it emulsifies). If the mixture is too thick, add a little bit of water and blend again until you reach the desired consistency.

3. Transfer the tahini to a serving bowl and stir in the parsley, if using. Enjoy!

NUTRITION · DATA FOR 1 SERVING:

Calories **57kcal**	Sodium **99mg**
Total Carbohydrates **5g**	Potassium **48mg**
Protein **1g**	Dietary Fiber **1g**
Total Fat **4g**	Sugars **1g**
Saturated Fat **1g**	Vitamin A **11% Daily Value**
Polyunsaturated Fat **1g**	Vitamin C **13% Daily Value**
Monounsaturated Fat **1g**	Calcium **38% Daily Value**
Trans Fat **1g**	Iron **20% Daily Value**
Cholesterol **0mg**	

Homemade Tahini Paste

Yield: ½ cup

INGREDIENTS

½ cup hulled sesame seeds

2–4 tbsp. olive oil

pinch of salt

INSTRUCTIONS

1. Grind the sesame seeds in a food processor and gradually add the oil until smooth. Mix in a pinch of salt.

2. Tip: Lightly toast the seeds in a dry pan on the stovetop before grinding for a deeper, nutty flavor. Don't toast the seeds in the oven as they can easily burn.

NUTRITION · DATA FOR 1 TABLESPOON:

Calories **59kcal**	Sodium **290mg**
Total Carbohydrates **2g**	Potassium **141mg**
Protein **1g**	Dietary Fiber **1g**
Total Fat **6g**	Sugars **0g**
Saturated Fat **1g**	Vitamin A **4.8% Daily Value**
Polyunsaturated Fat **2g**	Vitamin C **2.5% Daily Value**
Monounsaturated Fat **3g**	Calcium **2.6% Daily Value**
Trans Fat **0g**	Iron **5.3% Daily Value**
Cholesterol **35mg**	

Creamy Tahini Hummus

Yield: 3 cups

INGREDIENTS

¼ cup tahini paste

¼ cup lemon juice (from 1 large lemon)

2 tbsp. olive oil, plus more for serving

1 clove garlic

½ tsp. cumin

½ tsp. salt

1½ cups canned or cooked chickpeas, peeled and rinsed

2–3 tbsp. water, as needed

dash of paprika

INSTRUCTIONS

Combine the tahini and lemon juice in the bowl of a food processor and pulse to mix. Add the olive oil, garlic, cumin and salt and pulse until mixed. Add the chickpeas and pulse again until smooth. If the hummus is too thick, add the water a little at a time until you reach the desired consistency. Serve with a drizzle of olive oil and sprinkle the paprika over the top. Use veggies to dip!

NUTRITION · DATA FOR 1 SERVING (¼ CUP):

Calories **89kcal**	Sodium **18mg**
Total Carbohydrates **4g**	Potassium **8mg**
Protein **3g**	Dietary Fiber **2g**
Total Fat **9g**	Sugars **0g**
Saturated Fat **3g**	Vitamin A **1.3% Daily Value**
Polyunsaturated Fat **2g**	Vitamin C **3.5% Daily Value**
Monounsaturated Fat **3g**	Calcium **2.6% Daily Value**
Trans Fat **0g**	Iron **1.3% Daily Value**
Cholesterol **35mg**	

Beetroot Hummus

Yield: 1½ cups

INGREDIENTS

1 red beet

2 cloves garlic, peeled

2 tbsp. olive oil

1½ cups cooked or canned chickpeas, drained and rinsed

3 tbsp. warm water

2 tbsp. tahini paste

2 tbsp. lemon juice

½ tsp. cumin

½ tsp. coriander

salt and black pepper, to taste

INSTRUCTIONS

1. Preheat the oven to 400°F.

2. Place the beet and garlic cloves on a piece of foil and drizzle with the olive oil. Fold the foil over and seal into a packet, then place on a baking sheet. Transfer to the oven and roast for 30 minutes or until the beet is fork-tender. Carefully open the foil packet and let cool. When cool enough to handle, remove the beet skin. Place the beet and garlic cloves in the bowl of a food processor and blend. Continue blending while adding the rest of the ingredients for about 5 minutes. Keep in the fridge until ready to use. Serve with veggies!

NUTRITION · DATA FOR 1 SERVING (¼ CUP):

Calories **60kcal**	Sodium **93mg**
Total Carbohydrates **7g**	Potassium **14mg**
Protein **3g**	Dietary Fiber **1g**
Total Fat **3g**	Sugars **2g**
Saturated Fat **1g**	Vitamin A **6.1% Daily Value**
Polyunsaturated Fat **1g**	Vitamin C **5.8% Daily Value**
Monounsaturated Fat **1g**	Calcium **3.2% Daily Value**
Trans Fat **0g**	Iron **5% Daily Value**
Cholesterol **12mg**	

Chickpea Salad

Makes: 1 large salad or 2 small salads (2 servings)

INGREDIENTS

For the salad:
1 can (15 oz.) chickpeas,

½ cup sun-dried tomatoes

½ cucumber, diced

½ cup diced red onions

½ cup sliced olives

¼ cup parsley, chopped

¼ cup crumbled feta cheese

For the dressing:
¼ cup olive oil

2 tbsp. red wine vinegar

½ tsp. cumin

salt and black pepper, to taste

INSTRUCTIONS

1. Drain the can of chickpeas and transfer to a large bowl. Add the sun-dried tomatoes, cucumbers, onions, olives, parsley and feta cheese and stir to mix.

2. Combine all the dressing ingredients in a bowl. Refrigerate both the salad and the dressing for an hour before combining and serving.

NUTRITION · DATA FOR 1 SERVING:

Calories **166kcal**	Sodium **253mg**
Total Carbohydrates **20g**	Potassium **234mg**
Protein **4g**	Dietary Fiber **4g**
Total Fat **8g**	Sugars **0g**
Saturated Fat **1g**	Vitamin A **1.5% Daily Value**
Polyunsaturated Fat **1g**	Vitamin C **4.8% Daily Value**
Monounsaturated Fat **5g**	Calcium **3.8% Daily Value**
Trans Fat **0g**	Iron **7.1% Daily Value**
Cholesterol **0mg**	

Apple Slices with Almond Butter

Serves: 1

INGREDIENTS

1 apple

¼ cup almond butter

2 tbsp. sliced almonds

2 tbsp. walnuts

¼ cup dark chocolate chips

INSTRUCTIONS

Slice the apple crosswise. Spread each slice with almond butter and top with the almonds, walnuts and dark chocolate chips.

NUTRITION · DATA FOR 1 SERVING:

Calories **258kcal**	Sodium **7mg**
Total Carbohydrates **17g**	Potassium **8mg**
Protein **21g**	Dietary Fiber **10g**
Total Fat **56g**	Sugars **4.4g**
Saturated Fat **4g**	Vitamin A **0% Daily Value**
Polyunsaturated Fat **14g**	Vitamin C **0% Daily Value**
Monounsaturated Fat **30g**	Calcium **34% Daily Value**
Trans Fat **2g**	Iron **19% Daily Value**
Cholesterol **0mg**	

Plain Greek Yogurt and Fresh Berries

Serves: 1

INGREDIENTS

1 cup plain Greek yogurt

½ cup mixed berries (such as strawberries, blueberries or raspberries)

mint leaves (optional)

½ cup rolled oats

INSTRUCTIONS

Top the yogurt with your favorite berries and mint. Sprinkle rolled oats over top and add almonds for a flavor booster if desired

NUTRITION · DATA FOR 1 SERVING:

Calories **220kcal**	Sodium **115mg**
Total Carbohydrates **37g**	Potassium **78mg**
Protein **14g**	Dietary Fiber **3g**
Total Fat **4g**	Sugars **2g**
Saturated Fat **1g**	Vitamin A **3.7% Daily Value**
Polyunsaturated Fat **2g**	Vitamin C **2.5% Daily Value**
Monounsaturated Fat **1g**	Calcium **6.6% Daily Value**
Trans Fat **0g**	Iron **6.3% Daily Value**
Cholesterol **5mg**	

Dessert
RECIPES

Mediterranean Tiramisu

Serves: 4

INGREDIENTS

6 large egg yolks (approx. ½ cup)

1 cup sugar

1¼ cups mascarpone cheese, room temperature

1⅓ cups heavy whipping cream

1 cup cold espresso or strong coffee

½ cup coffee-flavored liqueur (optional)

30 Italian ladyfingers, Savoiardi style (about 1½ 7-oz. packages)

1 oz. unsweetened cocoa for dusting

INSTRUCTIONS

1. Combine the egg yolks and sugar in the top of a double boiler, set over boiling water and use a wire whisk to mix. Reduce the heat to low and cook, stirring constantly with the whisk, for about 10 minutes. This is your sabayon. Remove from the heat and continue to whisk until the yolks are thick and lemon-colored. Allow to cool briefly.

2. Add the room-temperature mascarpone cheese to the whipped yolks and whisk until well combined.

3. In a separate bowl, use an electric hand mixer or a stand mixer to whip the cream to stiff peaks.

4. Gently fold the whipped cream into the mascarpone-sabayon mixture and set aside.

5. Mix the cold espresso with the coffee liqueur, if using. Dip the ladyfingers into the mixture just long enough to get them wet. Do not soak them!

6. Arrange half of the ladyfingers in the bottom of a 9-inch-square baking dish or other similar-size container.

recipe continues

NUTRITION · DATA FOR 1 SERVING:

Calories **490kcal**	Sodium **200mg**
Total Carbohydrates **37g**	Potassium **176mg**
Protein **5g**	Dietary Fiber **10g**
Total Fat **34g**	Sugars **5g**
Saturated Fat **10g**	Vitamin A **7% Daily Value**
Polyunsaturated Fat **6g**	Vitamin C **12% Daily Value**
Monounsaturated Fat **14g**	Calcium **25% Daily Value**
Trans Fat **4g**	Iron **18% Daily Value**
Cholesterol **20mg**	

7. Spoon half the mascarpone cream filling over the ladyfingers.

8. Repeat the process with another layer of ladyfingers, and add another layer of mascarpone cream.

9. Dust the top with unsweetened cocoa and refrigerate for at least 4 hours, or ideally overnight.

Greek-Style, No-Bake Cheesecake with Yogurt

Serves: 4

INGREDIENTS

4 tbsp. butter, melted, plus more for the pan

1 (9-oz.) pkg. digestive biscuits

16 oz. cream cheese

5 oz. thick Greek yogurt

2 tbsp. honey

1 tsp. vanilla extract

4 oz. powdered sugar

9.5 oz. heavy cream

½ to 1 cup jam of your choice

INSTRUCTIONS

1. To make the base, butter a 9-inch removable-bottom pie tin. Place the biscuits in the bowl of a food processor and pulse until only crumbs remain. Transfer the crumbs to a bowl, then pour in the melted butter. Mix thoroughly until the crumbs are completely coated. Pour the mixture into the prepared pie tin and press firmly down into the base in an even layer. Place the tin in the fridge while you make the filling.

2. Combine the cream cheese, Greek yogurt, honey, vanilla and powdered sugar in a bowl, then beat with an electric mixer until smooth. Add the heavy cream and continue beating until the mixture is completely combined.

3. Pour the mixture into the biscuit crust and top the cheesecake with jam, to taste. Refrigerate overnight, or for at least 6 hours. Enjoy!

NUTRITION · DATA FOR 1 SERVING:

Calories **402kcal**	Sodium **400mg**
Total Carbohydrates **36g**	Potassium **348mg**
Protein **5g**	Dietary Fiber **0g**
Total Fat **9g**	Sugars **9g**
Saturated Fat **4g**	Vitamin A **13% Daily Value**
Polyunsaturated Fat **2g**	Vitamin C **9% Daily Value**
Monounsaturated Fat **3g**	Calcium **32% Daily Value**
Trans Fat **2g**	Iron **10% Daily Value**
Cholesterol **36mg**	

Greek Yogurt with Honey & Walnuts (Yiaourti Me Meli)

Serves: 1

INGREDIENTS

1 cup walnuts

½ cup honey

2½ cups Greek yogurt, strained

⅓ tsp. vanilla extract

cinnamon, ground

INSTRUCTIONS

1. Preheat the oven to 350°F.

2. Spread the walnuts in a single layer on a baking sheet and toast 7–8 minutes, or until they turn golden and fragrant. Transfer the toasted walnuts to a bowl, add the honey, and stir to coat. Set aside to cool down, 1–2 minutes.

3. In the meantime, stir together the Greek yogurt and vanilla extract and add to the bowl. Spoon the honey-walnut mixture over the yogurt and sprinkle with cinnamon.

4. Serve immediately or store in the fridge for up to 3 days. Enjoy!

NUTRITION · DATA FOR 1 SERVING:

Calories **284kcal**	Sodium **37mg**
Total Carbohydrates **27g**	Potassium **20mg**
Protein **12g**	Dietary Fiber **1g**
Total Fat **15g**	Sugars **24g**
Saturated Fat **4g**	Vitamin A **12% Daily Value**
Polyunsaturated Fat **8g**	Vitamin C **15% Daily Value**
Monounsaturated Fat **4g**	Calcium **22% Daily Value**
Trans Fat **0g**	Iron **19% Daily Value**
Cholesterol **13mg**	

Twisty Easter Cookies (Koulourakia)

Makes: 80 cookies

INGREDIENTS

1 cup butter, chopped, at room temperature

1½ cups sugar

½ cup milk

1½ tbsp. powdered baking ammonia (or baking powder)

4 medium eggs

1 tbsp. vanilla extract

zest of 2 oranges

2¼ lb. all-purpose flour

2 egg yolks

1 tbsp. water

INSTRUCTIONS

1. In a large mixing bowl, combine the butter and sugar in a stand mixer and mix 10–15 minutes, until the butter is creamy and fluffy.

2. In the meantime, warm the milk in a small saucepan until just lukewarm, then remove the pan from the heat. Add the baking ammonia and blend until dissolved. Set aside.

3. Add the eggs to the butter-sugar mixture one at a time while mixing, allowing for each one to be incorporated before adding the next. Add the vanilla extract, orange zest and the milk-ammonia mixture and mix to combine. Add the flour a little bit at a time and mix until the ingredients are combined and the dough is soft and not too sticky.

4. Cover the dough with plastic wrap and set aside to rest for 20 minutes.

5. Preheat the oven to 400°F.

recipe continues

NUTRITION · DATA FOR 1 SERVING (2 COOKIES):

Calories **88kcal**	Sodium **47mg**
Total Carbohydrates **14g**	Potassium **28mg**
Protein **2g**	Dietary Fiber **1g**
Total Fat **3g**	Sugars **4g**
Saturated Fat **2g**	Vitamin A **7% Daily Value**
Polyunsaturated Fat **1g**	Vitamin C **12% Daily Value**
Monounsaturated Fat **1g**	Calcium **27% Daily Value**
Trans Fat **0.1g**	Iron **13% Daily Value**
Cholesterol **28mg**	

6. Turn the dough out onto a clean working surface. Take a small piece of dough and form a log. Twist each end of the koulourakia in opposite directions. Line a large baking sheet with parchment paper and place the koulourakia on the sheet, leaving them 1 inch apart as they will rise a lot during the baking. Repeat with the remaining dough, working in batches depending on how many baking sheets you have.

7. In a small bowl, combine the egg yolks and water and whisk with a fork. Brush the tops of the koulourakia and bake for 15 minutes, until nice and golden!

8. Let the koulourakia cool completely on a wire rack and store in an airtight container for up to three weeks.

Frozen Blueberry Yogurt Swirl Pop Cups

Makes: 8

INGREDIENTS

2 cups blueberries

2 cups Greek yogurt

2 tbsp. agave or honey

1 drop liquid stevia

8 wooden craft sticks

INSTRUCTIONS

Blend the blueberries in a food processor or blender until they're like smoothies in consistency. Pour into a bowl and gently mix in the yogurt, agave or honey and stevia. Pour the mixture into an 8-popsicle mold and insert the wooden craft sticks. Freeze for at least 5 hours. When ready to serve, run under warm water to remove the popsicles from the mold.

NUTRITION · DATA FOR 1 SERVING:

Calories **120kcal**	Sodium **85mg**
Total Carbohydrates **18g**	Potassium **41mg**
Protein **4g**	Dietary Fiber **0g**
Total Fat **4g**	Sugars **2g**
Saturated Fat **2g**	Vitamin A **2.6% Daily Value**
Polyunsaturated Fat **1g**	Vitamin C **3.4% Daily Value**
Monounsaturated Fat **1g**	Calcium **6.4% Daily Value**
Trans Fat **1g**	Iron **7% Daily Value**
Cholesterol **15mg**	

Frozen Chocolate Bananas

Serves: 8

INGREDIENTS

4 bananas

8 wooden craft sticks

⅓ cup almond butter

¼ cup dark chocolate

½ cup almonds, chopped

INSTRUCTIONS

1. Cut bananas in half. Insert a wooden craft stick into the bottom of each banana. Freeze the bananas on a parchment-lined baking sheet for about 3 hours.

2. Spread the almond butter over each banana, then freeze for another hour.

3. Melt the chocolate in the top of a double boiler. Dip each banana into the chocolate. Spread the chopped almonds out on a plate and roll the chocolate-dipped bananas over the almonds to coat. Freeze again until the chocolate is firm, another 1–2 hours.

4. Tip: it's perfectly ok to substitute cashews or walnuts for the almonds if you prefer.

NUTRITION · DATA FOR 1 SERVING:

Calories **100kcal**	Sodium **7mg**
Total Carbohydrates **39g**	Potassium **21mg**
Protein **18g**	Dietary Fiber **2g**
Total Fat **6g**	Sugars **1g**
Saturated Fat **3g**	Vitamin A **4% Daily Value**
Polyunsaturated Fat **1g**	Vitamin C **7.1% Daily Value**
Monounsaturated Fat **2g**	Calcium **6% Daily Value**
Trans Fat **1g**	Iron **13% Daily Value**
Cholesterol **0mg**	

Chocolate Chia Pudding with Raspberries

Serves: 4

INGREDIENTS

1½ cups almond milk

¼ cup dark chocolate chips

3 tbsp. chia seeds

¼ cup raspberries

¼ cup almonds

8 mint leaves (optional)

INSTRUCTIONS

Combine 1 cup of the almond milk and the chocolate chips in a pot over low heat. Stir to melt the chocolate slowly, making sure not to scald the milk. Stir in the remaining milk and let cool to room temperature. Pour the chocolate mixture into 4 serving glasses and fold in the chia seeds. Let stand for 15 minutes, then stir again. Cover and transfer to the refrigerator for at least 8 hours. When ready to serve, stir the chia seed mixture and top with the raspberries, almonds and mint leaves, if using.

NUTRITION · DATA FOR 1 SERVING:

Calories **220kcal**	Sodium **90mg**
Total Carbohydrates **28g**	Potassium **81mg**
Protein **6g**	Dietary Fiber **2g**
Total Fat **11g**	Sugars **3g**
Saturated Fat **3g**	Vitamin A **3% Daily Value**
Polyunsaturated Fat **4g**	Vitamin C **4.6% Daily Value**
Monounsaturated Fat **2g**	
Trans Fat **2g**	Calcium **2.6% Daily Value**
Cholesterol **35mg**	Iron **8% Daily Value**

Chia Seed & Mango Purée with Blueberries

Serves: 2

INGREDIENTS

¼ cup chia seeds

1½ cups almond milk

1 tbsp. honey or agave

½ tsp. vanilla extract

1 drop liquid stevia

1 mango, peeled and pit removed

½ cup blueberries

2 mint leaves

INSTRUCTIONS

Mix the chia seeds, almond milk, honey or agave, vanilla extract and stevia in a bowl until combined. Allow the chia seed mixture to soak for 2 hours in the refrigerator. Purée the mango in a food processor or blender. Fold the mango purée into the chia seed mixture. Divide between two serving dishes and garnish with the blueberries and mint.

NUTRITION · DATA FOR 1 SERVING:

Calories **341kcal**	Sodium **141mg**
Total Carbohydrates **44g**	Potassium **76mg**
Protein **14g**	Dietary Fiber **19g**
Total Fat **28g**	Sugars **34g**
Saturated Fat **14g**	Vitamin A **6% Daily Value**
Polyunsaturated Fat **6g**	Vitamin C **11% Daily Value**
Monounsaturated Fat **8g**	Calcium **24% Daily Value**
Trans Fat **0g**	Iron **15% Daily Value**
Cholesterol **0mg**	

Caramelized Pear with Gorgonzola

Serves: 2

INGREDIENTS

2 tbsp. olive oil

1 ripe pear, cored and sliced

¼ cup gorgonzola cheese

¼ cup Natural Caramel Sauce (recipe follows)

3 tbsp. honey or agave

alfalfa sprouts (optional)

INSTRUCTIONS

Heat the olive oil in a pan over medium heat. Add the pear and cook until lightly browned, about 5–7 minutes. Add the gorgonzola cheese, gently stir and continue cooking until the cheese begins to melt, about 3–5 minutes. Divide the pear slices between 2 plates and garnish with the caramel sauce, honey and sprouts, if using.

NUTRITION · DATA FOR 1 SERVING:

Calories **260kcal**	Sodium **31mg**
Total Carbohydrates **39g**	Potassium **23mg**
Protein **22g**	Dietary Fiber **4g**
Total Fat **18g**	Sugars **14g**
Saturated Fat **5g**	Vitamin A **4% Daily Value**
Polyunsaturated Fat **11g**	Vitamin C **14% Daily Value**
Monounsaturated Fat **2g**	Calcium **16% Daily Value**
Trans Fat **0g**	Iron **11% Daily Value**
Cholesterol **0mg**	

Natural Caramel Sauce

Makes: 1 jar (6 fl oz.)

INGREDIENTS

¼ cup, plus 2 tbsp. powdered erythritol

¼ cup water

2 tbsp. maple syrup

¼ cup butter

⅓ cup heavy cream

INSTRUCTIONS

Combine the erythritol, water and maple syrup in a medium saucepan over medium heat and bring to a boil. Add the butter and whisk for about 10 minutes until the mixture begins to brown. Turn off the heat and add in the cream. Turn the heat to medium-high and whisk for 2 minutes. Once the sauce begins to thicken and reaches the consistency of caramel sauce, turn off the heat completely. Serve immediately, or transfer to a jar and store for up to 1 week.

NUTRITION · DATA FOR 1 SERVING:

Calories **80kcal**	Sodium **65mg**
Total Carbohydrates **39g**	Potassium **25mg**
Protein **11g**	Dietary Fiber **2g**
Total Fat **3g**	Sugars **0g**
Saturated Fat **1g**	Vitamin A **3% Daily Value**
Polyunsaturated Fat **1g**	Vitamin C **7% Daily Value**
Monounsaturated Fat **1g**	Calcium **15% Daily Value**
Trans Fat **0g**	Iron **5% Daily Value**
Cholesterol **0mg**	

Chocolate Chip Cookies

Makes: 2 dozen

INGREDIENTS

2½ cups Swerve sugar replacement

1 cup olive oil

1 tbsp. vanilla extract

1 tsp. salt

1 large egg

2 cups flour

½ tsp. baking soda

2 cups unsweetened chocolate chips

INSTRUCTIONS

1. Preheat the oven to 350°F and line two baking sheets with parchment paper.

2. Combine the Swerve, oil, vanilla extract and salt in a large bowl and mix until smooth. Mix in the egg. In a separate bowl, combine the flour and baking soda. Combine the wet and dry ingredients, then fold in the chocolate chips.

3. Form the dough into 1-inch balls and place them on the prepared baking sheets, pressing down slightly and leaving 1 inch between the cookies to allow them to expand.

4. Bake until the cookies are golden brown around the edges, about 10 minutes. Cool on a rack before serving.

NUTRITION · DATA FOR 1 SERVING (4 COOKIES):

Calories **400kcal**	Sodium **214mg**
Total Carbohydrates **58g**	Potassium **135mg**
Protein **6g**	Dietary Fiber **5g**
Total Fat **29g**	Sugars **2g**
Saturated Fat **14g**	Vitamin A **6% Daily Value**
Polyunsaturated Fat **5g**	Vitamin C **5.7% Daily Value**
Monounsaturated Fat **8g**	Calcium **24% Daily Value**
Trans Fat **0g**	Iron **16% Daily Value**
Cholesterol **70mg**	

Lemon Bars with Tahini Crust

Makes: 12 bars

INGREDIENTS

For the tahini crust:
½ cup rolled oats

½ cup sesame seeds

8 dates

¼ cup tahini

¼ tsp. salt

For the lemon filling:
1 cup fresh lemon juice

14 oz. firm tofu

¼ cup, plus 1 tbsp. Swerve sugar replacement

1 tbsp. arrowroot starch

¼ tbsp. lemon zest

INSTRUCTIONS

1. Preheat the oven to 350°F and line an 8-inch baking dish with parchment paper.

2. Combine the oats and sesame seeds in the bowl of a food processor and pulse for 30 seconds. Add the dates, tahini and salt and blend until combined, about 90 seconds. Press the mixture down into the prepared baking dish until evenly distributed. Press to pack it down. Bake until the edges are golden brown, about 15 minutes.

3. Combine the lemon juice, tofu, Swerve, arrowroot starch and lemon zest in food processor until smooth. Pour onto the baked crust and bake for an additional 35 minutes. Let cool, then refrigerate for about 90 minutes until the custard is set. Cut into 12 squares and lift out, using the parchment paper.

NUTRITION · DATA FOR 1 SERVING (1 BAR):

Calories **189kcal**	Sodium **45mg**
Total Carbohydrates **15g**	Potassium **41mg**
Protein **7g**	Dietary Fiber **2g**
Total Fat **6g**	Sugars **0g**
Saturated Fat **3g**	Vitamin A **3% Daily Value**
Polyunsaturated Fat **1g**	Vitamin C **8.3% Daily Value**
Monounsaturated Fat **1g**	Calcium **4.6% Daily Value**
Trans Fat **1g**	Iron **12% Daily Value**
Cholesterol **0mg**	

Pistachio Pudding

Serves: 6

INGREDIENTS

1 cup shelled unsalted pistachios, plus more for garnish

½ cup Swerve sugar replacement

2 cups, plus 2 tbsp. almond milk

1 egg, plus 2 egg yolks

2 tbsp. maple syrup

dash of salt

2 tbsp. olive oil

¼ tbsp. vanilla extract

INSTRUCTIONS

1. Blend the pistachios in a food processor until finely ground. Add ¼ cup of Swerve and 2 tablespoons of the almond milk. Pulse until a paste forms. Transfer the paste to a saucepan and add the remaining 2 cups of almond milk. Cook over medium-high heat until the mixture begins to steam.

2. Meanwhile, in the food processor, blend the remaining ¼ cup of Swerve with the whole egg, egg yolks, maple syrup and salt. With the processor still running, slowly add ½ cup of the warm milk mixture to temper the eggs so that the mixture does not curdle.

3. Slowly add the contents of the food processor back into the pan with the milk mixture and continue to cook. Reduce the heat to medium and cook until the pudding begins to bubble and thicken, about 6–8 minutes. Remove from the heat and add the oil and vanilla. Divide into 6 serving cups, and chill for at least 4 hours or overnight. Serve cold, garnished with chopped pistachios.

NUTRITION · DATA FOR 1 SERVING:

Calories **100kcal**	Sodium **90mg**
Total Carbohydrates **24g**	Potassium **37mg**
Protein **1g**	Dietary Fiber **1g**
Total Fat **1g**	Sugars **2g**
Saturated Fat **1g**	Vitamin A **7% Daily Value**
Polyunsaturated Fat **1g**	Vitamin C **5% Daily Value**
Monounsaturated Fat **0.1g**	Calcium **8% Daily Value**
Trans Fat **0g**	Iron **4% Daily Value**
Cholesterol **0mg**	

Index

Index

JOURNAL

Tear Off Weekly Shopping Lists

WEEK

Shopping List

Vegetables

- 1 lb. arugula
- 3 avocados
- 4 bell peppers
- 1 butternut squash
- 1 lb. carrots
- 1 lb. celery
- 2 oz. chives
- 1 lb. corn
- 1 large cucumber
- 8 oz. green beans
- 1 lb. green onions
- 2 lb. lettuce (mixed greens)
- 1 lb. mushrooms
- 2 lb. potatoes
- 1 lb. red onions
- 2 scallions
- 1 lb. spinach
- 2 lb. yellow onions
- 2 lb. zucchini

Fruit

- 3 apples
- 4 oz. cherry tomato
- 2 lemons
- 2 Nashi pears
- 2 pomegranate arils
- 3 medium tomatoes

Protein

- 4 lb. chicken breast
- 4 oz. chorizo
- 2 cod fillets
- 6 eggs
- 1 lb. flounder
- 1 lb. ground beef
- 1 lb. ground pork
- 2 lamb racks
- 1 lb. prawns
- 2 oz. prosciutto
- 4 salmon fillets
- 2 sausages

Pantry Items
(make sure you have at least the following on hand)

- ½ cup balsamic vinegar
- 1 cup black olives
- 4 oz. canned green lentils
- 2 oz. capers
- 2 qt. chicken stock
- 8 oz. chickpeas
- 1 cup couscous
- ¼ cup Dijon mustard
- 2 oz. dried apricots
- ½ cup dried cranberries
- 4 oz. flaxseed sprouts
- ½ cup honey
- ½ cup lemon juice
- 4 oz. millet

- ○ 8 oz. oats
- ○ 1 cup olive oil
- ○ 4 oz. pearl barley
- ○ 4 oz. polenta
- ○ ¼ cup prepared mustard
- ○ 6 oz. raisins
- ○ 12 oz. rice
- ○ 4 oz. sun-dried tomatoes
- ○ ½ cup tahini (sesame paste)
- ○ 1 can tomatoes
- ○ 2 cans tuna
- ○ 2 qt. vegetable stock
- ○ ¼ cup walnuts
- ○ ¼ cup white wine vinegar
- ○ 1 cup whole-wheat flour
- ○ ¼ cup Worcestershire sauce

Dry Herbs, Spices and Baking Needs

- ○ baking powder
- ○ basil
- ○ bay leaves
- ○ black pepper
- ○ cilantro
- ○ dried marjoram
- ○ dried mustard
- ○ dried oregano leaves
- ○ dried porcini mushrooms
- ○ fennel seeds
- ○ flour
- ○ garlic powder
- ○ ground cinnamon
- ○ ground cumin
- ○ Italian dried herbs
- ○ lemon verbena
- ○ mint
- ○ oregano

- ○ paprika
- ○ parsley
- ○ rosemary sprigs
- ○ saffron
- ○ salt
- ○ sugar
- ○ thyme

Dairy *(substitute as needed)*

- ○ butter
- ○ feta cheese
- ○ Greek feta cheese
- ○ Greek yogurt
- ○ Italian ricotta cheese
- ○ milk
- ○ mozzarella cheese
- ○ Parmesan cheese
- ○ ricotta cheese

Bakery and Frozen Items

- ○ bread crumbs
- ○ pie crust
- ○ sourdough bread
- ○ toast
- ○ tortillas

Alcohol Used for Cooking

- ○ Madeira wine
- ○ white wine

WEEK 2

Shopping List

Fruit

- 4 oz. fresh figs
- 4 frozen bananas
- 2 lemons
- 4 oz. cherry tomato
- 3 medium tomatoes
- 2 Nashi pears
- 2 pomegranate arils

Protein

- 2 cod fillets
- 6 eggs
- 1 lb. flounder
- 1 lb. ground beef
- 1 lb. ground pork
- 2 lamb racks
- 8 oz. lobster
- 1 lb. prawns
- 2 oz. prosciutto
- 4 salmon fillets
- 2 sausages

Pantry

- ½ cup balsamic vinegar
- 1 cup black olives
- 4 oz. canned green lentils
- 2 oz. capers
- 2 qt. chicken stock
- 8 oz. chickpeas
- 1 cup couscous
- 2 oz. dried apricots
- ½ cup dried cranberries
- 4 oz. flaxseed sprouts
- ½ cup honey
- ½ cup lemon juice
- 4 oz. millet

Vegetables

- 1 lb. arugula
- 2 lb. asparagus
- 3 avocados
- 8 oz. baby sweet peas
- 1 butternut squash
- 1 lb. carrots
- 1 lb. celery
- 2 oz. chives
- 8 oz. green beans
- 1 lb. green onions
- 1 large cabbage
- 1 large cucumber
- 2 lb. lettuce (mixed greens)
- 1 lb. mushrooms
- 4 bell peppers
- 2 lb. potatoes
- 1 lb. red onions
- 2 scallions
- 1 lb. spinach
- 2 lb. yellow onions
- 2 lb. zucchini

- 8 oz. oats
- 1 cup olive oil
- 4 oz. pearl barley
- 4 oz. polenta
- ¼ cup prepared mustard
- 6 oz. raisins
- 12 oz. rice
- 4 oz. sundried tomatoes
- ½ cup tahini (sesame paste)
- 1 can tomatoes
- 2 cans tuna
- 2 qt. vegetable stock
- ¼ cup walnuts
- ¼ cup white wine vinegar
- 1 cup whole-wheat flour
- ¼ cup Worcestershire sauce

Dry Herbs, Spices and Baking Needs

- baking powder
- basil
- bay leaves
- black pepper
- cilantro
- dried marjoram
- dried oregano leaves
- dried porcini mushrooms
- fennel seed
- garlic powder
- lemon verbena
- mint
- oregano
- paprika
- parsley
- rosemary sprigs
- saffron
- salt
- sugar
- thyme

Dairy

- butter
- cream cheese
- feta cheese
- Greek yogurt
- heavy cream
- Italian ricotta
- milk
- mozzarella cheese
- Parmesan cheese
- ricotta cheese

Bakery and Frozen Items

- bread crumbs
- pie crust
- sourdough bread
- toast
- tortillas

Alcohol Used for Cooking

- white wine

WEEK 3

Shopping List

Vegetables

- 1 lb. arugula
- 2 lb. asparagus
- 3 avocados
- 8 oz. baby sweet peas
- 4 bell peppers
- 8 oz. bulgur wheat
- 1 butternut squash
- 1 lb. carrots
- 1 lb. celery
- 2 oz. chives
- 6 oz. edamame
- 8 oz. green beans
- 1 lb. green onions
- 1 large cabbage
- 1 large cucumber
- 2 lb. lettuce (mixed greens)
- 1 lb. mushrooms
- 2 lb. potatoes
- 1 lb. red onions
- 2 scallions
- 1 lb. spinach
- 2 lb. yellow onions
- 2 lb. zucchini

Fruit

- 2 oz. currents
- 4 oz. figs
- 4 oz. fresh figs
- 4 frozen bananas
- 2 lemons
- 4 oz. blueberries
- 4 oz. cherry tomato
- 3 medium tomatoes

Protein

- 4 oz. anchovy fillets
- 4 lb. chicken breasts
- 8 oz. chorizo
- 2 cod fillets
- 1 lb. flounder
- 1 lb. ground beef
- 1 lb. ground pork
- 4 Italian sausages
- 2 lamb racks
- 8 oz. lobster
- 1 lb. prawns
- 2 oz. prosciutto
- 4 salmon fillets
- 8 oz. squid

Pantry

- ½ cup almonds
- ½ cup balsamic vinegar
- 2 qt. beef stock
- 1 cup black olives
- 4 oz. canned green lentils
- 2 oz. capers
- 2 qt. chicken stock
- 8 oz. chickpeas
- 1 cup couscous
- ¼ cup Dijon mustard
- 2 oz. dried apricots
- ½ cup dried cranberries

- 4 oz. flaxseed sprouts
- ½ cup honey
- ½ cup lemon juice
- 4 oz. millet
- 8 oz. oats
- 1 cup olive oil
- 4 oz. pearl barley
- 4 oz. polenta
- ¼ cup prepared mustard
- 6 oz. raisins
- 12 oz. rice
- ½ cup smoked almonds
- 1 cup spelt flour
- 4 oz. sun-dried tomatoes
- ½ cup tahini (sesame paste)
- 1 can tomato paste
- 1 can tomatoes
- 2 cans tuna
- 1 tbsp. vanilla extract
- 2 qt. vegetable stock
- ¼ cup walnuts
- ¼ cup white wine vinegar
- 1 cup whole-wheat flour
- 2 cups whole-wheat gnocchi
- 2 cups whole-wheat orzo pasta
- ¼ cup Worcestershire sauce

Dry Herbs, Spices and Baking

- baking powder
- basil
- bay leaves
- black pepper
- cilantro
- dried marjoram
- dried oregano leaves
- dried porcini mushrooms
- fennel seeds
- garlic powder
- glemon verbena

- mint
- oregano
- paprika
- parsley
- rosemary sprigs
- saffron
- salt
- sugar
- thyme

Dairy

- butter
- cream cheese
- feta cheese
- Greek yogurt
- heavy cream
- Italian ricotta cheese
- milk
- mozzarella cheese
- Parmesan cheese
- ricotta cheese

Bakery and Frozen Items

- bread crumbs
- pie crust
- sourdough bread
- toast
- tortillas

Alcohol Used for Cooking

- Curaçao liqueur
- Madeira wine
- red wine (dry)
- sherry
- white wine

WEEK

Shopping List

Vegetables

- 1 lb. arugula
- 2 lb. asparagus
- 3 avocados
- 8 oz. baby sweet peas
- 2 lb. beets
- 4 bell peppers
- 1 butternut squash
- 1 lb. carrots
- 1 lb. celery
- 2 oz. chives
- 8 oz. dried porcini mushrooms
- 2 fennel bulbs
- 8 oz. green beans
- 1 lb. green onions
- 1 lb. kale
- 1 large cabbage
- 1 large cucumber
- 2 lb. lettuce (mixed greens)
- 2 medium eggplants
- 1 lb. mushrooms
- 2 lb. potatoes
- 1 lb. red onions
- 2 scallions
- 1 lb. spinach
- 2 lb. yellow onions
- 2 lb. zucchini

Fruit

- 4 oz. fresh figs
- 4 frozen bananas
- 2 lemons
- 4 oz. cherry tomato
- 3 medium tomatoes
- 2 Nashi pears
- 2 pomegranate arils

Protein

- 1 lb. beef fillet
- 4 lb. chicken breasts
- 8 oz. chorizo
- 1 lb. flounder
- 1 lb. ground beef
- 1 lb. ground pork
- 1 halibut fillet
- 4 Italian sausages
- 2 oz. prosciutto
- 8 oz. squid
- 2 lb. tiny clams or mussels
- 8 oz. turkey breast

Pantry

- ½ cup almonds
- ½ cup balsamic vinegar
- 2 qt. beef stock
- 1 cup black olives
- 4 oz. canned green lentils
- 2 oz. capers
- 2 qt. chicken stock
- 8 oz. chickpeas
- 1 cup couscous
- ¼ cup Dijon mustard
- 2 oz. dried apricots
- ½ cup dried cranberries

- 4 oz. flaxseed sprouts
- ½ cup honey
- ½ cup lemon juice
- 4 oz. millet
- 8 oz. oats
- 1 cup olive oil
- 4 oz. pearl barley
- 4 oz. polenta
- ¼ cup prepared mustard
- 6 oz. raisins
- 12 oz. rice
- ½ cup smoked almonds
- 4 oz. sundried tomatoes
- ½ cup tahini (sesame paste)
- 1 can tomato paste
- 1 can tomatoes
- 2 cans tuna
- 2 qt. vegetable stock
- ¼ cup walnuts
- ¼ cup white wine vinegar
- 1 cup whole-wheat flour
- ¼ cup Worcestershire sauce

Dry Herbs, Spices and Baking Needs

- baking powder
- basil
- bay Leaves
- black pepper
- cilantro
- dried marjoram
- dried oregano leaves
- dried porcini mushrooms
- fennel seeds
- garlic powder
- ground cinnamon

- ground cumin
- Italian dried herbs
- mint
- oregano
- paprika
- parsley
- rosemary sprigs
- saffron
- salt
- sugar
- thyme

Dairy

- butter
- cream cheese
- feta cheese
- Greek yogurt
- heavy cream
- Italian ricotta cheese
- milk
- mozzarella cheese
- Parmesan cheese
- ricotta cheese

Bakery and Frozen Items

- bread crumbs
- pie crust
- toast
- tortillas

Alcohol Used for Cooking

- Curaçao liqueur
- red wine
- white wine

WEEK 5 Shopping List

Vegetables

- 1 lb. arugula
- 2 lb. asparagus
- 3 avocados
- 8 oz. baby sweet peas
- 4 bell peppers
- 1 butternut squash
- 1 lb. carrots
- 1 lb. celery
- 2 oz. chives
- 2 fennel bulbs
- 8 oz. green beans
- 1 lb. green onions
- 1 lb. kale
- 1 large cabbage
- 1 large cucumber
- 2 lb. lettuce (mixed greens)
- 2 medium eggplants
- 1 lb. mushrooms
- 2 lb. potatoes
- 1 lb. red onions
- 2 scallions
- 1 lb. spinach
- 2 lb. sweet potatoes
- 2 lb. yellow onions
- 2 lb. zucchini

Fruit

- 4 oz. fresh figs
- 4 frozen bananas
- 2 lemons
- 4 oz. cherry tomato
- 3 medium tomatoes
- 4 oz. raspberries
- 4 oz. strawberries

Protein

- 4 oz. anchovy fillets
- 1 lb. beef fillets
- 4 lb. chicken breasts
- 6 chicken thighs
- 8 oz. chorizo
- 1 lb. flounder
- 1 lb. ground beef
- 1 lb. ground lamb
- 1 lb. ground pork
- 1 halibut fillet
- 4 Italian sausages
- 2 oz. prosciutto
- 8 oz. squid
- 2 lb. tiny clams or mussels
- 8 oz. turkey breast

Pantry

- ½ cup almonds
- ½ cup balsamic vinegar
- 2 qt. beef stock
- 1 cup black olives
- 4 oz. canned green lentils
- 2 oz. capers
- 2 qt. chicken stock
- 8 oz. chickpeas
- 1 cup couscous
- ¼ cup Dijon mustard
- 2 oz. dried apricots
- ½ cup dried cranberries
- 4 oz. flaxseed sprouts

- ○ ½ cup honey
- ○ ½ cup lemon juice
- ○ 4 oz. millet
- ○ 8 oz. oats
- ○ 1 cup olive oil
- ○ 4 oz. pearl barley
- ○ 4 oz. polenta
- ○ ¼ cup prepared mustard
- ○ 6 oz. raisins
- ○ 12 oz. rice
- ○ ½ cup smoked almonds
- ○ 1 cup spelt flour
- ○ 4 oz. sun-dried tomatoes
- ○ ½ cup tahini (sesame paste)
- ○ 1 can tomato paste
- ○ 1 can tomatoes
- ○ 2 cans tuna
- ○ 1 tbsp. vanilla extract
- ○ 2 qt. vegetable stock
- ○ ¼ cup walnuts
- ○ ¼ cup white wine vinegar
- ○ 1 cup whole-wheat flour
- ○ 2 cups whole-wheat gnocchi
- ○ 2 cups whole-wheat orzo pasta
- ○ ¼ cup Worcestershire sauce

Dry Herbs, Spices and Baking Needs

- ○ baking powder
- ○ basil
- ○ bay leaves
- ○ black pepper
- ○ cilantro
- ○ dried marjoram
- ○ dried oregano leaves
- ○ dried porcini mushrooms
- ○ fennel seed
- ○ garlic powder
- ○ ground cinnamon

- ○ ground cumin
- ○ Italian dried herbs
- ○ lemon verbena
- ○ mint
- ○ oregano
- ○ paprika
- ○ parsley
- ○ rosemary sprigs
- ○ saffron
- ○ salt
- ○ sugar
- ○ thyme

Dairy

- ○ butter
- ○ cream cheese
- ○ feta cheese
- ○ Greek yogurt
- ○ heavy cream
- ○ Italian ricotta cheese
- ○ milk
- ○ mozzarella cheese
- ○ Parmesan cheese
- ○ ricotta cheese

Bakery and Frozen Items

- ○ bread crumbs
- ○ pie crust
- ○ sourdough bread
- ○ toast
- ○ tortillas

Alcohol Used for Cooking

- ○ white wine (dry)

WEEK 6

Shopping List

Vegetables

- 1 lb. arugula
- 2 lb. asparagus
- 8 oz. baby sweet peas
- 4 bell peppers
- 1 butternut squash
- 1 lb. carrots
- 1 lb. celery
- 2 oz. chives
- 8 oz. green beans
- 1 lb. green onions
- 1 large cabbage
- 1 large cucumber
- 2 lb. lettuce (mixed greens)
- 2 medium eggplants
- 1 lb. mushrooms
- 2 lb. potatoes
- 1 lb. red onions
- 2 scallions
- 1 small watermelon
- 1 lb. spinach
- 2 lb. yellow onions
- 2 lb. zucchini

Fruit

- 4 oz. fresh figs
- 4 frozen bananas
- 2 lemons
- 4 oz. cherry tomato
- 3 medium tomatoes
- 1 small clam raspberries
- 1 small clam strawberries

Protein

- 4 oz. anchovy fillets
- 1 lb. beef fillet
- 4 lb. chicken breasts
- 6 chicken thighs
- 8 oz. chorizo
- 1 lb. ground beef
- 1 lb. ground lamb
- 1 lb. ground pork
- 1 halibut fillet
- 4 Italian sausages
- 8 oz. shrimp
- 8 oz. turkey breast

Pantry

- ½ cup balsamic vinegar
- 2 qt. beef stock
- 1 cup black olives
- 4 oz. canned green lentils
- 2 oz. capers
- 2 qt. chicken stock
- 8 oz. chickpeas
- 1 cup couscous
- ¼ cup Dijon mustard
- 2 oz. dried apricots
- ½ cup dried cranberries
- 4 oz. flaxseed sprouts
- ½ cup honey

- ½ cup lemon juice
- 4 oz. millet
- 8 oz. oats
- 1 cup olive oil
- 4 oz. pearl barley
- 4 oz. polenta
- ¼ cup prepared mustard
- 6 oz. raisins
- 12 oz. rice
- ½ cup smoked almonds
- 1 cup spelt flour
- 4 oz. sun-dried tomatoes
- ½ cup tahini (sesame paste)
- 1 can tomato paste
- 1 can tomatoes
- 2 cans tuna
- 1 tbsp. vanilla extract
- 2 qt. vegetable stock
- ¼ cup walnuts
- ¼ cup white wine vinegar
- 1 cup whole-wheat flour
- 2 cups whole-wheat gnocchi
- 2 cups whole-wheat orzo pasta
- ¼ cup Worcestershire sauce

Dry Herbs, Spices and Baking Needs

- baking powder
- basil
- bay leaves
- black pepper
- cilantro
- dried marjoram
- dried oregano leaves
- dried porcini mushrooms

- fennel seeds
- garlic powder
- ground cinnamon
- ground cumin
- Italian dried herbs
- lemon verbena
- mint
- oregano
- paprika
- parsley
- rosemary sprigs
- saffron
- salt
- sugar
- thyme

Dairy

- butter
- cream cheese
- feta cheese
- Greek yogurt
- heavy cream
- Italian Ricotta
- milk
- mozzarella cheese
- Parmesan cheese
- ricotta cheese

Bakery and Frozen Items

- bread crumbs
- pie crust
- sourdough bread
- toast
- tortillas

WEEK

7

Shopping
List

Vegetables

- 1 lb. arugula
- 2 lb. asparagus
- 3 avocados
- 8 oz. baby sweet peas
- 4 bell peppers
- 1 butternut squash
- 1 lb. carrots
- 1 lb. celery
- 2 oz. chives
- 2 fennel bulbs
- 8 oz. green beans
- 1 lb. green onions
- 1 lb. kale
- 1 large cabbage
- 1 large cucumber
- 2 lb. lettuce (mixed greens)
- 2 medium eggplants
- 3 medium pickles
- 1 lb. mushrooms
- 2 lb. potatoes
- 1 lb. red onions
- 2 scallions
- 1 lb. spinach
- 2 lb. sweet potatoes
- 2 lb. yellow onions
- 2 lb. zucchini

Fruit

- 4 oz. fresh figs
- 4 frozen bananas
- 2 lemons
- 4 oz. cherry tomato
- 3 medium tomatoes
- 4 oz. raspberries
- 4 oz. strawberries

Protein

- 4 lb. chicken breasts
- 4 eggs
- 2 fish fillets
- 1 lb. lobster
- 4 oz. prosciutto
- 2 salmon fillets
- 8 oz. shrimp
- 1 lb. tiny clams
- 8 oz. turkey breast

Pantry

- ½ cup almonds
- ½ cup balsamic vinegar
- 2 qt. beef stock
- 1 cup black olives
- 4 oz. canned green lentils
- 2 oz. capers
- 2 qt. chicken stock
- 8 oz. chickpeas
- 1 cup couscous
- ¼ cup Dijon mustard
- 2 oz. dried apricots
- ½ cup dried cranberries
- 4 oz. flaxseed sprouts

- ○ ½ cup honey
- ○ ½ cup lemon juice
- ○ 4 oz. millet
- ○ 8 oz. oats
- ○ 1 cup olive oil
- ○ 1 cup orange juice
- ○ ½ cup pearl barley
- ○ 4 oz. polenta
- ○ ¼ cup prepared mustard
- ○ 6 oz. raisins
- ○ 12 oz. rice
- ○ ½ cup smoked almonds
- ○ 1 cup spelt flour
- ○ 4 oz. sun-dried tomatoes
- ○ ½ cup tahini (sesame paste)
- ○ 1 can tomato paste
- ○ 1 can tomatoes
- ○ 2 cans tuna
- ○ 1 tbsp. vanilla extract
- ○ 2 qt. vegetable stock
- ○ ¼ cup walnuts
- ○ ¼ cup white wine vinegar
- ○ 1 cup whole-wheat flour
- ○ 2 cups whole-wheat gnocchi
- ○ 2 cups whole-wheat orzo pasta
- ○ ¼ cup Worcestershire sauce

Dry Herbs, Spices and Baking Needs

- ○ baking powder
- ○ basil
- ○ bay leaf
- ○ black pepper
- ○ cilantro
- ○ dried marjoram
- ○ dried oregano leaves
- ○ dried porcini mushrooms
- ○ fennel seeds

- ○ garlic powder
- ○ ground cinnamon
- ○ ground cumin
- ○ Italian dried herbs
- ○ lemon verbena
- ○ mint
- ○ oregano
- ○ paprika
- ○ parsley
- ○ rosemary sprigs
- ○ saffron
- ○ salt
- ○ sugar
- ○ thyme

Dairy

- ○ butter
- ○ cream cheese
- ○ feta cheese
- ○ Greek yogurt
- ○ heavy cream
- ○ Italian ricotta cheese
- ○ milk
- ○ mozzarella cheese
- ○ Parmesan cheese
- ○ ricotta cheese

Bakery

- ○ crusty bread
- ○ French bread
- ○ pie crust
- ○ sheet puff pastry

Alcohol Used for Cooking

- ○ white wine